EUROPEAN CROWNS

1700 — 1800

JOHN S. DAVENPORT

SPINK & SON LTD.

5 - 7, KING ST.,
ST. JAMES'S,
LONDON, S.W.1

1964

FOREWORD

A second edition of this work allows me to make a number of corrections, include a few additions, and add four new illustrations. I should again be glad to hear from anyone who has a specimen or a picture of the few types which still remain unillustrated.

The inclusion of the Austrian-Habsburg pieces in a non-German book will probably raise many European eyebrows, but having separated them previously in my first volume and knowing that American collectors will not be confused by my arrangement, I can only say that the decision was quite arbitrary—as well as convenient—and that the issues of the Holy Roman Emperors, the Austrian princes and counts, the Austrian Church states, the Austrian and Spanish Netherlands, Holstein, Liechtenstein, Liege, and Luxemburg could quite properly have been included with the Germanic issues of the Holy Roman Empire. Geography has possibly triumphed over history.

The list of those to whom I am indebted is again long and distinguished. I have leaned heavily on the resources and personnel of the American Numismatic Society and wish to thank Geoffrey H. North, Richard P. Breaden, Henry Grunthal and William L. Clark, the latter especially for his help in the Turkish series, for their forbearance and advice. The manuscript was virtually in final form before I was able to inspect personally the collections of the numerous European museums I visited during 1958-59, but I had corresponded for some years with many members of the various staffs and obtained information and photographs. To the entire personnel of the Coins and Medals Department of the British Museum I wish to express my appreciation for their patient and courteous attention to my many questions and requests. Dr. H. Enno van Gelder of the Koninklijk Penningkabinet in The Hague was most kind in allowing me to use a manuscript covering all modern Dutch coinage. Dr. Willy Schwabacher of the Kungl. Myntkabinettet in Stockholm, Frau Dr. Fritze Lindahl of the Nationalmuseet in Copenhagen, Dr. Bernhard Koch of the Kunsthistorisches Museum in Vienna, Dr. Peter Jaeckel of the Staatliche Münzsammlung in Munich, Dr. D. Schwarz of the Schweizerisches Landesmuseum in Zürich, Dr. Gert Hatz of the Hamburg Münzkabinett were especially helpful in assisting me to solve my problems. To curators and staff members of the museums in Amsterdam, Utrecht, Brussels, Geneva, Bern, Basel, Frankfurt, Brunswick, Budapest, and Prague I am also much indebted for information, casts, photographs, and advice. Many coin dealers kindly opened their libraries and their stocks for my inspection, and I would like to express my gratitude to several staff members in Spink's and Seaby's in London, to the Santamarias in Rome, to Erich Cahn in Basel, to Frank Sternberg in Zürich, to Jacques Schulman and Leonard Forrer in Amsterdam, and to Paul Tinchant in Brussels for the generous use of their time and resources.

Many private collectors have answered queries or provided coins for photographing. Energetic in my behalf have been Andrew E. Kelpsh, William R. Higgins, Jr., Tyge Sondergaard, Carl O. Schwab, Joseph F. Sawicki, R. H. Rosholm, Robert Prann, and many others, to all of whom go my thanks. To all those who have added to the information in this book since its original publication I am also very grateful.

Again may I ask anyone discovering any remaining errors of omission or commission to please let me know.

Knox College,
Galesburg, Ill.
October, 1964.

European Crowns, 1700—1800

Valuations—November, 1968

Many coins of this series appear but rarely on the market. Actual prices realized for any given coin may vary widely in practice, even in the case of relatively common pieces. The estimates given here should therefore be taken as a very general guide, applicable in each case to the commonest variety in attractive condition.

Pieces marked with an asterisk bear prices over £200 ($480) and are those whose prices fluctuate too much at the present state of the market to give an estimate.

	£	$		£	$		£	$		£	$		£	$
1001	12	29	1036	15	36	1071	28	67	1106	38	91	1142	45	108
1002	25	60	1037	15	36	1072	55	132	1107	100	240	1143	38	91
1003	15	36	1038	15	36	1073	55	132	1109	45	108	1144	28	67
1004	7	17	1039	23	55	1074	75	180	1110	35	84	1145	28	67
1005	25	60	1040	23	55	1075	28	67	1111	22	53	1146	15	36
1006	35	84	1041	23	55	1076	28	67	1112	22	53	1147	15	36
1007	28	67	1042	23	55	1077	90	216	1113	90	216	1148	15	36
1008	28	67	1043	23	55	1078	18	43	1114	22	53	1149	15	36
1009	28	67	1044	*	*	1079	28	67	1115	22	53	1150	12	29
1010	38	91	1045	90	216	1080	25	60	1116	18	43	1151	12	29
1011	28	67	1046	35	84	1081	22	53	1117	10	24	1152	18	43
1012	*	*	1047	100	240	1082	28	67	1118	110	264	1153	18	43
1013	15	36	1048	100	240	1083	22	53	1119	110	264	1154	18	43
1014	18	43	1049	55	132	1084	22	53	1120	22	53	1155	15	36
1015	25	60	1050	12	29	1085	28	67	1121	22	53	1156	15	36
1016	75	180	1051	12	29	1086	22	53	1122	18	43	1157	15	36
1017	*	*	1052	80	192	1087	22	53	1123	18	43	1158	20	48
1018	20	48	1053	15	36	1088	45	108	1124	12	29	1159	20	48
1019	60	144	1054	15	36	1089	28	67	1125	22	53	1160	38	91
1020	50	120	1055	15	36	1090	33	79	1126	28	67	1161	15	36
1021	65	156	1056	12	29	1091	33	79	1127	28	67	1162	150	360
1022	60	144	1057	80	192	1092	22	53	1128	18	43	1163	38	91
1023	60	144	1058	35	84	1093	22	53	1129	18	43	1164	15	36
1024	35	84	1059	12	29	1094	28	67	1130	18	43	1165	28	67
1025	28	67	1060	12	29	1095	75	180	1131	18	43	1166	15	36
1026	28	67	1061	80	192	1096	23	55	1132	18	43	1167	18	43
1027	50	120	1062	12	29	1097	75	180	1133	10	24	1168	10	24
1028	38	91	1063	50	120	1098	28	67	1134	110	264	1169	10	24
1029	45	108	1064	45	108	1099	*	*	1135	*	*	1170	10	24
1030	45	108	1065	75	180	1100	80	192	1136	18	43	1171	80	192
1031	45	108	1066	28	67	1101	28	67	1137	90	216	1172	80	192
1032	*	*	1067	28	67	1102	28	67	1138	33	79	1173	45	108
1033	115	276	1068	75	180	1103	38	91	1139	18	43	1174	90	216
1034	115	276	1069	28	67	1104	28	67	1140	15	36	1175	15	36
1035	12	29	1070	28	67	1105	*	*	1141	48	115	1176	25	60

	£	$		£	$		£	$		£	$		£	$
1177	90	216	1225	15	36	1273	*	*	1320	50	120	1366	35	84
1178	55	132	1226	15	36	1274	*	*	1321	60	144	1367	*	*
1179	55	132	1227	45	108	1275	*	*	1322	50	120	1368	*	*
1180	10	24	1228	35	84	1276	*	*	1323	*	*	1369	40	96
1181	65	156	1229	35	84	1277	*	*	1324	35	84	1370	20	48
1182	35	84	1230	35	84	1278	55	132	1325	30	72	1371	100	240
1183	35	84	1232	45	108	1279	28	67	1326	35	84	1372	*	*
1184	45	108	1233	45	108	1280	15	36	1327	35	84	1373	12	29
1185	*	*	1234	15	36	1281	20	48	1328	30	72	1374	12	29
1186	150	360	1235	*	*	1282	10	24	1329	25	60	1375	15	36
1187	150	360	1236	18	43	1283	10	24	1330	20	48	1376	10	24
1188	100	240	1237	35	84	1284	10	24	1331	20	48	1377	55	132
1189	100	240	1238	35	84	1285	45	108	1332	13	31	1378	*	*
1190	110	264	1239	35	84	1286	12	29	1332A	25	60	1379	50	120
1191	60	144	1240	35	84	1287	45	108	1333	20	48	1380	75	180
1192	80	192	1241	35	84	1288	*	*	1334	20	48	1381	*	*
1193	120	288	1242	30	72	1289	45	108	1335	30	72	1382	*	*
1194	90	216	1243	55	132	1290	23	55	1336	20	48	1383	*	*
1195	90	216	1244	55	132	1291	20	48	1337	15	36	1384	*	*
1196	75	180	1245	55	132	1292	15	36	1338	60	144	1385	*	*
1197	75	180	1246	65	156	1293	*	*	1339	120	288	1386	38	91
1198	*	*	1247	13	31	1294	28	67	1340	50	120	1387	40	96
1199	85	204	1248	15	36	1295	65	156	1341	40	96	1388	20	48
1200	45	108	1249	15	36	1296	55	132	1342	40	96	1389	25	60
1201	55	132	1250	15	36	1297	100	240	1343	40	96	1390	20	48
1202	65	156	1251	15	36	1298	100	240	1344	40	96	1391	45	108
1203	65	156	1252	15	36	1299	35	84	1345	90	216	1392	100	240
1204	*	*	1253	15	36	1300	38	91	1346	95	228	1393	65	156
1205	28	67	1254	15	36	1301	38	91	1347	90	216	1394	50	120
1206	28	67	1255	15	36	1302	38	91	1348	70	168	1395	100	240
1207	18	43	1256	18	43	1303	50	120	1349	75	180	1396	30	72
1208	18	43	1257	22	53	1304	38	91	1350	85	204	1397	45	108
1209	18	43	1258	15	36	1305	65	156	1351	115	176	1398	30	72
1211	18	43	1259	15	36	1306	18	43	1352	75	180	1399	25	60
1212	20	48	1260	65	156	1307	18	43	1353	70	168	1400	30	72
1213	28	67	1261	15	36	1308	18	43	1354	50	120	1401	25	60
1214	15	36	1262	22	53	1309	28	67	1355	75	180	1402	25	60
1215	15	36	1263	10	24	1310	55	132	1356	*	*	1403	70	168
1216	15	36	1264	10	24	1311	18	43	1357	25	60	1404	50	120
1217	*	*	1265	12	29	1312	65	156	1358	60	144	1405	30	72
1218	15	3 6	1266	*	*	1313	15	36	1359	15	36	1406	30	72
1219	15	36	1267	50	120	1314	20	48	1360	*	*	1407	50	120
1220	15	36	1268	55	132	1315	18	43	1361	*	*	1408	70	168
1221	15	36	1269	28	67	1316	40	96	1362	*	*	1409	20	48
1222	*	*	1270	28	67	1317	*	*	1363	120	288	1410	80	192
1223	15	36	1271	*	*	1318	*	*	1364	65	156	1411	140	336
1224	45	108	1272	*	*	1319	*	*	1365	45	108	1412	55	132

	£	$		£	$		£	$		£	$		£	$
1413	*	*	1460	90	216	1509	20	48	1555	80	192	1602	27	65
1414	*	*	1461	90	216	1510	15	36	1556	*	*	1603	30	72
1415	42	100	1462	120	288	1511	45	108	1557	40	96	1604	20	48
1416	130		1463	60	144	1512	90	216	1558	*	*	1605	25	60
1417	18	43	1464	90	216	1513	60	144	1559	75	180	1606	25	60
1418	18	43	1465	90	216	1514	20	48	1560	*	*	1607	25	60
1419	20	48	1466	120	288	1515	12	29	1561	35	84	1608	20	48
1420	*		1467	120	288	1516	15	36	1562	50	120	1609	20	48
1421	18	43	1468	75	180	1517	15	36	1563	40	96	1610	10	24
1422	*		1469	75	180	1518	25	60	1564	25	60	1611	15	36
1423	30	72	1470	75	180	1519	35	84	1565	90	216	1612	*	*
1424	35	84	1471	30	72	1520	100	240	1566	*	*	1613	50	120
1425	20	48	1472	*	*	1521	25	60	1567	30	72	1614	60	144
1426	*	*	1473	60	144	1523	*	*	1568	35	84	1615	*	*
1427	120	288	1474	40	96	1524	65	156	1569	*	*	1616	*	*
1428	150	360	1475	80	192	1525	65	156	1570	40	96	1617	60	144
1429	150	360	1478	*	*	1526	*	*	1571	*	*	1618	50	120
1430	*	*	1479	*	*	1527	30	72	1572	90	216	1619	30	72
1431	*		1480	50	120	1528	*	*	1573	*	*	1620	25	60
1432	65	156	1481	40	96	1529	*	*	1574	40	96	1621	28	67
1433	140	336	1482	*	*	1530	30	72	1575	25	60	1622	65	156
1434	90	216	1483	*		1531	65	156	1576	70	168	1623	20	48
1435	150	360	1484	*		1532	*	*	1577	40	96	1624	60	144
1436	170	408	1485	140	336	1533	25	60	1578	80	192	1625	*	*
1437	170	408	1486	60	120	1534	*	*	1579	50	120	1627	25	60
1438	100	240	1487	*	*	1535	65	156	1580	70	168	1628	12	29
1439	150	360	1488	*	*	1536	100	240	1581	*	*	1629	12	29
1440	*		1489	*	*	1537	50	120	1582	*	*	1630	12	29
1441	90	216	1490	*	*	1538	40	96	1583	45	108	1631	8	19
1442	110	264	1491	*	*	1539	100	240	1584	45	108	1632	8	19
1443	150	360	1492	*	*	1540	25	60	1585	55	132	1633	10	24
1444	*	*	1493	*	*	1541	60	144	1586	*	*	1635	55	132
1445	200	480	1494	70	168	1542	100	240	1587	40	96	1636	25	60
1446	*		1495	45	108	1543	25	60	1588	40	96	1637	25	60
1447	100	240	1496	80	192	1543A	*	*	1589	48	115	1638	*	*
1448	160	384	1497	160	384	1544	50	120	1590	55	132	1639	15	36
1449	100	240	1498	35	84	1545	90	216	1591	50	120	1640	20	48
1450	100	240	1499	38	91	1546	*	*	1592	100	240	1641	20	48
1451	100	240	1500	50	120	1547	25	60	1593	55	132	1642	80	192
1452	100	240	1501	50	120	1548	40	96	1594	55	132	1643	35	84
1453	90	216	1502	*		1549	80	192	1595	55	132	1644	*	*
1454	90	216	1503	*		1550	*	*	1596	55	132	1645	48	115
1455	*		1504	30	72	1551	30	72	1597	55	132	1646	*	*
1456	90	216	1505	15	36	1552	55	132	1598	40	96	1647	*	*
1457	100	240	1506	35	84	1553	65	156	1599	35	84	1648	*	*
1458	90	216	1507	25	60	1553A	*	*	1600	18	43	1649	*	*
1459	150	360	1508	50	120	1554	80	192	1601	25	60	1650		

	£	$		£	$		£	$		£	$		£	$
1651	*	*	1699	45	108	1746	20	48	1794	25	60	1841	18	43
1652	35	84	1700	33	79	1747	20	48	1795	25	60	1842	28	67
1653	28	67	1701	25	60	1748	*	*	1796	25	60	1843	18	43
1654	28	67	1702	35	84	1749	70	168	1797	25	60	1844	25	60
1655	30	72	1703	35	84	1750	25	60	1798	25	60	1845	10	24
1656	35	84	1704	40	96	1751	25	60	1799	25	60	1846	18	43
1657	35	84	1705	35	84	1752	25	60	1800	7	17	1847	40	96
1658	35	84	1706	30	72	1753	*	*	1801	9	22	1848	10	24
1659	45	108	1707	30	72	1754	25	60	1802	13	31	1849	12	29
1660	30	72	1708	15	36	1755	20	48	1803	18	43	1850	12	29
1661	38	91	1709	15	36	1756	25	60	1804	7	17	1851	18	43
1662	35	84	1710	*	*	1757	25	60	1805	6	14	1852	10	24
1663	90	216	1711	*	*	1758	35	84	1806	7	17	1853	10	24
1664	22	53	1712	100	240	1759	40	96	1807	6	14	1854	35	84
1665	22	53	1713	150	360	1760	50	120	1808	14	34	1855	35	84
1666	*	*	1714	160	384	1761	*	*	1809	18	43	1856	35	84
1667	20	48	1715	60	144	1762	*	*	1810	10	24			
1668	20	48	1716	100	240	1763	*	*	1811	10	24			
1669	20	48	1717	40	96	1764	150	360	1812	9	22			
1670	30	72	1718	150	360	1766	*	*	1813	18	43			
1671	20	48	1719	55	132	1767	20	48	1814	10	24			
1672	20	48	1720	30	72	1768	20	48	1815	7	17			
1673	20	48	1721	*	*	1769	25	60	1816	13	31			
1674	25	60	1722	70	168	1770	25	60	1817	13	31			
1675	16	38	1723	30	72	1771	80	192	1818	12	29			
1676	110	264	1724	100	240	1772	100	240	1819	12	29			
1677	25	60	1725	110	264	1773	200	480	1820	*	*			
1678	25	60	1726	110	264	1774	80	192	1821	18	43			
1679	28	67	1727	30	72	1775	25	60	1822	18	43			
1680	170	408	1728	35	84	1776	120	288	1823	60	144			
1681	25	60	1729	*	*	1777	*	*	1824	18	43			
1682	85	204	1730	35	84	1778	30	72	1825	110	264			
1683	25	60	1731	45	108	1779	28	67	1826	50	120			
1684	25	60	1732	45	108	1780	*	*	1827	18	43			
1685	30	72	1733	30	72	1781	50	120	1828	55	132			
1686	25	60	1734	60	144	1782	70	168	1829	22	53			
1687	100	240	1735	15	36	1783	30	72	1830	22	53			
1688	25	60	1736	15	36	1784	25	60	1831	45	108			
1690	*	*	1737	30	72	1785	45	108	1832	15	36			
1691	90	216	1738	30	72	1786	30	72	1833	55	132			
1692	*	*	1739	*	*	1787	25	60	1834	15	36			
1693	100	240	1740	100	240	1788	25	60	1835	45	108			
1694	*	*	1741	120	288	1789	25	60	1836	15	36			
1695	120	288	1742	75	180	1790	25	60	1837	20	48			
1696	30	72	1743	20	48	1791	25	60	1838	28	67			
169?	45	108	1744	20	48	1792	200	480	1839	45	108			
		108	1745	20	48	1793	25	60	1840	18	43			

TABLE OF CONTENTS

PREFACE

SINCE there is considerably more variety in size and weight in the general European coinages than in the German, even with the several systems which existed within the Holy Roman Empire, I have drawn a line at about 20 grams in weight for inclusion and exclusion regardless of size. This has not always been rigidly followed as the Swedish 4 marks weighing 21 grams have been omitted since there are larger pieces in the Swedish coinage, but the Portuguese 400 reis weighing only about 15 grams have been included as their largest silver coin. Most of the rejected pieces are mentioned or described in Appendix C.

A few technicalites in my earlier books have sometimes been misunderstood. LEO(POLD) means that the inscription appears sometimes as LEO and sometimes as LEOPOLD. There are occasionally as many as four spellings of one word. A dash indicates a break in the legend at that point, and / indicates the end of a line of inscription on the coin. ET and AE when written as ligatures have had to be rendered as separate letters. F or f frequently after engravers' initials means **fecit**, made by the die cutter or engraver. Double numbers [ ] mean that this same design appeared in an earlier volume with the number in brackets and is therefore not to be regarded as a new type.

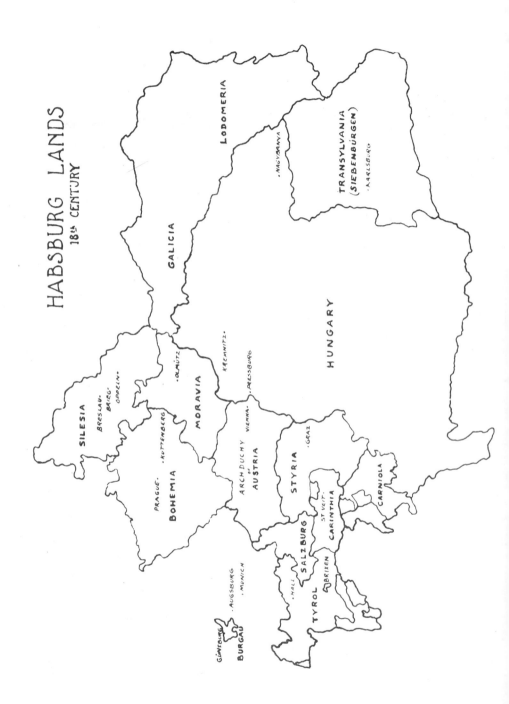

HABSBURG LANDS
18ᵗʰ CENTURY

SILESIA
BRESLAU-
BRIEG-
OPPELN-

BOHEMIA
PRAGUE-
-KUTTENBERG

MORAVIA
-OLMÜTZ

GALICIA

LODOMERIA

-MAGYBANYA

TRANSYLVANIA
(SIEBENBÜRGEN)
-KARLSBURG

HUNGARY

KREMNITZ-

ARCHDUCHY
OF
AUSTRIA
VIENNA- -PRESSBURG

STYRIA
-GRAZ

CARNIOLA

CARINTHIA
ST VEIT-

SALZBURG

TYROL
-BRIXEN

-HALL

BURGAU
GÜNZBURG-
-AUGSBURG
-MUNICH

AUSTRIA

THE duchies of Austria, Styria, Carinthia, and Carniola came under control of the Habsburg family after the extinction of the Babenburg line of Austrian dukes in the thirteenth century. Family prestige was established by continuous election from 1438 on, except for a brief interval, of the head of the house as Holy Roman Emperor, and family possessions increased as Alsace, Burgundy, Bohemia, Moravia, Silesia, Tyrol, and Hungary, thru inheritance, election, or conquest, were added to their holdings.

Shaken by the Thirty Years War (1618-1648), the Habsburg family's personal possessions, which had been consolidated and essentially separated from the Imperial possessions, enjoyed a period of increasing strength and stability under Leopold I (1658-1705), who added Transylvania to his lands about 1690. Leopold died in the midst of the War of the Spanish Succession, which persisted during the short reign of his son Joseph I (1705-1711). The Treaty of Utrecht was finally signed in 1713 after Charles VI (1711-1740) had become Emperor. Charles had been the Habsburg candidate for the throne of Spain and his succession to the Austrian throne upset some of his allies who did not want to see the two thrones united. By the Treaty of Rastatt the following year, Charles abandoned his claim to Spain and gave up his remaining holdings in Alsace, but received in compensation Milan, Sardinia, Naples, and part of Tuscany as well as the Spanish Netherlands, now to be called the Austrian Netherlands.

Further territorial changes in his reign included the exchange of Sardinia for Sicily (see Naples-Sicily) with the Duke of Savoy in 1720. Struggle over the election of his Saxon candidate for the throne of Poland ultimately cost him the loss of Novara and Tortona to Savoy and Naples-Sicily and his portions of Tuscany to the Spanish king's son. In compensation he acquired the Italian duchies of Parma and Piacenza. The last years of his reign saw the cession of Bosnia, Serbia, and Wallachia to Turkey.

Partly responsible for Charles' persistent setbacks was his all engrossing policy of assuring the Habsburg succession to his daughter Maria Theresia as the male line of the family was coming to an end. After his death in 1740 Maria Theresia succeeded in Austria, Bohemia, and Hungary, but several of the Powers which had guaranteed the Pragmatic Sanction, greedy for land, now claimed various Habsburg territories and the War of the Austrian Succession (1740-1748) ensued. When the final peace was concluded at Aix-la-Chapelle in 1748, Prussia had gained Silesia; and Parma, Piacenza, and Guastalla had been ceded to the Spanish Infante, Philip. One consolation was achieved. Francis Stephen, duke of Lorraine, who had agreed to an exchange of Lorraine for Tuscany upon his marriage to Maria Theresia in 1736, had been elected and crowned emperor in 1745.

The Seven Years War (1756-1763), in spite of new alliances, especially with France, failed to alter the basic situation; and Francis died in 1765 to be succeeded by his son Joseph as Holy Roman Emperor. Joseph II (1765-1790) acted as co-regent with his mother in the Habsburg dominions. The War of the Bavarian Succession in 1777 added the Inn Quarter to Austrian lands, all other claims to Bavaria being abandoned. The partitions of Poland in 1772 and 1795 brought the territories of Zips, Galicia, and Lodomeria in the former year and West Galicia in the latter.

Joseph II succeeded to all the family domains on the death of his mother in 1780 and proceeded to push a drastic program of governmental, social, agrarian, and religious reform. He was too liberal for his times, moved too rapidly, and antagonized too many influential groups. After rebellion had flared in the Netherlands and Hungary, the emperor shortly before his death was obliged to abandon a number of his plans.

His brother Leopold (1790-1792), erstwhile duke of Tuscany, inherited a dangerous situation and proceeded as rapidly as possible to stabilize his position both at home and abroad, by undoing much of what his brother had attempted.

His son Francis II (1792-1835) found himself involved during much of the first half of his reign in the wars with France and Napoleon. He lost Belgium in 1795 and

Milan and Mantua, but received part of the Venetian Republic when Napoleon abolished it in 1797. The first phase of Francis' career came to an end when he assumed the title of Emperor of Austria in 1804 and abandoned the titles of King of Germany and Holy Roman Emperor, in his family since 1273, in 1806.

My usual procedure of arranging the coins by date has been abandoned, and the Austrian series is listed by mints. The order of the mints follows Miller zu Aichholz, as the standard authority, though it has no virtue for American collectors except a geographic or historical one. The order is roughly the mints first of the hereditary Habsburg lands, then Hungary, Bohemia, Silesia (until 1740), Siebenbürg (Transyivania), Burgau, and finally the temporary ones. Though the distinguishing feature of each mint is usually its coat of arms, each often has, mint initials and a different legend on the reverse. In the notes which introduce the coins of each ruler, these features have been selected as the quickest and surest means of identification. The corresponding numbers in the text have been added for quick reference.

LEOPOLD I 1657-1705

	Arms	Reverse legend	Initials	Numbers
Vienna	multiple	— COM. TYROL		(1001)
Graz	lion (above)	— BVRG. STYRIAE EC.		(1002)
Hall	eagle (center)	— COM. TYR.		(1003)
Kremnitz	2 part on 4 part	— CO. TYR.	K.B.	(1004)
Nagybanya	same	— CO. TY.	N.B.	(1005)
Prague	lion	— BOHEMIAE REX	G.E	(1006-8)
Oppeln	multiple	— BVRG ET SILESIAE	F.N	(1009-10)
Breslau	multiple	— BVRG ET SILESIAE	F.N	(1010-11)
Brieg			C B	(1012)

1001   TALER 1701-1705 (VIENNA)

LEOPOLDUS. D:G - ROM. IMP. S.A. GE. HU. BO: REX., bust R.

ARCHIDVX. AVSTRIAE. DVX. BVR. COM. TYROL., date, crowned double eagle with arms on breast.

The harness differs slightly from date to date. The 1701 has larger letters and different curls.

The 1701 and 1703 have LEOPOLDVS. The 1701, 1703, 1705 have HV.

1002   TALER 1705 (GRAZ)

LEOPOLDVS. D:G: - decoration ROM: IMP: S:A:G:H:ET: BO: REX. palm, bust R.
.ARCHID: AVS: DVX - BVRG: STYRIAE. EC. 17 - 05, crowned arms with cherubs above, all
in chain. Shield with Styrian lion surmounting.

1003   TALER 1701, 1704 (HALL)

LEOPOLDVS. D:G: ROM: IMP: SE: A:G:H:B: REX., bust R.
ARCHID: AVST: - DVX: BV: COM: TYR: divided date, crowned arms in chain with Tyrolian
eagle in center.
Several varieties of each date. The 1701 with initials IAK. A 1705 has been reported.

1004   TALER 1703 (KREMNITZ)

LEOPOLD: (arms) D:G:R:I:S:A: GER: HVN: (arms) BO: REX., bust R.
ARCHIDVX. AVS: DVX. BVR: MAR: MOR: CO: TYR: 1703, crowned double eagle with arms
on breast. K - B below.

1005.   TALER 1702-1703 (NAGYBANYA)
LEOPOLDVS. (arms) D.G. RO. I.S. AVG. GER. (arms) HV. BO. REX., bust R.
ARCHIDVX. AVS. DVX. BVR. MAR. MOR. CO. TY. divided date, arms similar to #1004 with
initials N - B below.
The 1702 has ICB way up in bust; the 1703 does not.

1006   TALER 1702 (PRAGUE)
LEOPOLDUS. D:G: ROMAN: IMPERA: S:A., bust R.
GERM: HUNG: & - BOHEMIAE. REX. 17 - 02., crowned double eagle with Bohemian lion on
breast. G.E. below.

1007   TALER 1703-1704 (PRAGUE)
Similar to #1006 with new bust in different harness.
Similar to #1006 with larger lion in arms.
The two dates differ in many details. The 1704 has IMPER.

1008 **TALER 1705 (PRAGUE)**
LEOPOLDUS. D:G. - ROMANOR: IMPER: S:A., new bust R.
Similar to #1006, eagle's tail does not break border, smaller lion, and G:E in cartouche at bottom.

1009 **TALER 1701-1702 (OPPELN)**
LEOPOLDUS. DG. ROM: IMP: SEM: AVG: GER: HU: ET. BO: REX., bust R.
ARCHIDUX. AVSTRIAE. - DUX. BVRG. ET. SILESIAE. divided date, crowned double eagle with arms on breast. F.N. in cartouche below.

1010 **TALER 1703 (OPPELN), 1704 (BRESLAU)**
LEOPOLDVS. DG. ROM: - IMP: SEM: AVG: GER: HU: BO: REX., bust R.
Similar to #1009, eagles without haloes, new tail, and different cartouche for initials.

1011   TALER 1705 (BRESLAU)
Similar to #1010, new bust with LEOPOLDUS and HV, different punctuation.
Similar to #1010, haloes on eagles and new tail, AUSTRIAE and BURG.

1012   TALER 1705 (BRIEG)
Saurma #681.

JOSEPH I 1705-1711

	Arms	Reverse legend	Intials	Numbers
Vienna	two part	— COM. TYROL		(1013-14)
Graz	lion (above)	— BVRGV: STYRIAE EC.		(1015)
Hall	eagle (one head)	— COM. TYR(OLIS)		(1016-18)
		— COMES TIROL		
Kremnitz	2 part on 4 part	— CO. TYR.	K.B.	(1019-21)
Pressburg	same or Austrian on	— CO. TY.	CH, C.S.H,	
	Hungarian arms		PW	(1022-23)
Prague	lion (only)	— BOHEMIAE REX	P.M	(1024-26)
			G.E.	
Kuttenberg	same	— BOHEMIAE REX	B W	(1027)
Breslau	2 part on 4 part or	— BURG (V). ET(&)	F.N,	
	Austrian-Burgundian	SILESIAE	G.H.	(1028-31)
	arms			
Brieg			CB	(1032)
Munich	Austrian-Burgundian	— ARCHIDUX	*	(1033-34)
	arms	AUSTRIAE &		

1013   TALER 1705-1710 (VIENNA)
IOSEPHUS. D.G. RO - .IMP. S.A. GER. - HV: BO: REX., bust R with I.M.H. in garment fold.
ARCHIDVX. AVSTRIAE. DVX. BVR. COM. TYROL. date, crowned eagle with two part arms
on breast.
Small differences in bust, armor, and punctuation.

1014   TALER 1710-1711 (VIENNA)
Similar to #1013 but no beaded border. Initials I.M.H. or M.H.
Similar to #1013 but no beaded border.

1015   TALER 1706 (GRAZ)
IOSEPHVS. D:G: ROm: - :IMP: S:A: GER: - HV: ET: BO: REX., bust R.
ARCHID: AVST: DVX. - BVRGV: STYRIAE. EC. 17 - 06, crowned arms in chain. Above
cupids and shield with Styrian lion.

1016   2 TALER N.D. (HALL)
IOSEPHUS. D:G: ROM: IMP: SE: AV - G: HV: BO: REX., bust R.
ARCHIDVX: AVST: DVX: BVR: COM: TYROLIS, crowned Tyrolian eagle with l   in
wreath.
There is also a larger size piece of 4 taler weight.

1017   2 TALER N.D. (HALL)
Similar to #1016.
DVX. BVRGVNDIAE. COMES. TIROL, crowned Tyrolian eagle in beaded border.

1018   TALER 1706-1707, 1710-1711 (HALL)

Similar to #1016 with AV or AV. or AV: or AU:
ARCHID: AVST: - DVX: BV: COM: TYR. divided date., crowned arms in chain.
Harness slightly changed on 1710-1711. Variety 1706 with IAK on edge.
A 1705 has also been reported.

TALER 1709 (KREMNITZ)

IOSEPHUS (arms) D:G:R:I:S:A:G - (arms) H:B: REX., bust R in border.
ARCHIDVX. AVS: DVX. BVR: MAR: MOR: CO: TYR: 1709, crowned double eagle with arms
on breast. K - B below.

1020   TALER 1709 (KREMNITZ)

IOSEPHUS. (arms) D:G:R:I:S:A: GE: HV - (arms) BO: REX., bust R, no border.
Similar to #1019.

B

1021   TALER 1711 (KREMNITZ)

IOSEPH: D:G:R. (arms) I:S: - A: (arms) G:H:B: REX., bust R.
ARCHID: AVS: D: BV: - M: MOR: CO: TY:1711., crowned double eagle with arms on breast.
K - B below.

1022   TALER 1705-1706 (PRESSBURG)

IOSEPHUS (arms) D:G.R.I.S. AV. GE. (arms) HV. B(U:). REX, bust R.

ARCHID. AV. DV. BV. MAR. MOR. CO. TY. divided date, crowned double eagle with four part
arms on breast. Below C - H and C S H under the tail.

1023   TALER 1706-1708, 1710-1711 (PRESSBURG)

Similar to #1022, changed bust with I.G.S. below.
Similar to #1022, two part oval shield with C - H below.
Changed bust without initials in 1711. The 1706-1708 have C.S.H on the reverse. The 1710-1711
have P W

1024   TALER 1706 (PRAGUE)
IOSEPHUS. D:G: ROMAN: IM - P: SEMPER. A:, bust R.
GERMAN: HUNGAR: - ET: BOHEMIAE. REX. 17 - 06., crowned double eagle with Bohemian
lion on breast. G.E in cartouche below tail.

1025   TALER 1706-1707 (PRAGUE)
IOSEPHUS. D:G.(:) - ROMAN: IMP.(:) - SEMPER. AV:, bust R.
Similar to #1024 with G.E. in different cartouche.
The 1707 has different drapery and the reverse is much more like #1024.

1026   TALER 1709-1710 (PRAGUE)
IOSEPHUS. D:G: - ROM: IMP: - SEMP: AU., bust R.
GERMAN: HUNG: - ET. BOHEMIAE. REX. divided date., arms similar to #1025.
Both dates come with the initials G.E or P.M.

1027   TALER 1711 (KUTTENBERG)
IOSEPHUS. D :G : - ROM: IMPER. - SEMP : AUG., bust R.
Similar to #1024 with smaller lion arms and B x W below.

1028   TALER 1706 (BRESLAU)
IOSEPHUS. DG. ROMA: IMPERATOR: SEM. AV. GE. HV. BO. REX., bust R.
ARCHIDVX. AUSTRIAE. - DUX. BURG. ET SILESIAE. 17 - 06.,crowned double eagle with
four part arms on breast. F.N in cartouche below.

1029   TALER 1707-1708 (BRESLAU)
IOSEPHUS. DG. ROM. IMP. SEM. AUG. GER. HV. BO. REX., bust R.
Similar to #1028 but with two part arms. The 1707 has AVSTRIAE and small AE in SILESIAE.
   The 1708 has AVSTRI:
The two busts differ.

1030 **TALER 1709 (BRESLAU)**

IOSEPHUS. DG. ROM. - IMP. SEM. AU. - GE. H.B. REX., new bust R with GH.
Similar to #1028 with four part arms and legend BURGU: & SILESIae.

1031 **TALER 1710-1711 (BRESLAU)**

IOSEPHVS. DG. ROM. - IMP. SEM. A.G.H.B. REX., new bust R.
Similar to #1030 with V's for U's, ET for & and SILESIA.

1032 **TALER 1705-1706 (BRIEG)**

1033   TALER 1705 (MUNICH)

IOSEPHVS. D.G. - R.I.S.A.G.H.B.Rx, bust R with ⁕ below.
ARCHIDVX - AVSTRIAE &. 17 - 05⁕, crowned double eagle with two part arms on breast and ⁕ below.
A. Another bust with four lines of armor on arm.

1034   TALER 1705 (MUNICH)

Similar to #1033 with changed robes.
Similar to #1033 with legend unbroken at bottom.

CHARLES VI   1711-1740

	Arms	Reverse legend	Initials	Numbers
Vienna	Austrian arms	— BU(RG) COM. TYROL:		(1035-38)
Graz	lion	— STYRIAE (EC)		(1039-43)
St. Veit	2 part on 4 part	— CARINTHIAE		(1044-48)
Hall	eagle	— BU(RG) COM. TYR(OL) (IS)		(1049-56)
Kremnitz	2 part on 4 part	— M. MOR. CO(M). TY.	K.B.	(1057-62)
Pressburg	2 part or 2 part on 4 part	— MAR. MOR. CO. TY. — AVST: D: BURGVN.	C.H. P.W.	(1063-64)
Prague	lion	— BOHEMIAE REX — SIL(E) (S) MAR(G) M(OR). — M. MOR. CO. TY. —BU. COM. TYROL	I.A.P.	(1065-87)
	2 arms	— AUSBEUT THALER		
Kuttenberg	large lion	— BOHEMIAE REX	B.W.	(1088)
Breslau	eagle	— BUR. & SIL.(E) (S) (IAE)		(1089-98)
Brieg	2 part on 4 part	— FOD. REICHSTEIN	C.B.	(1099)
Siebenbürgen	half bird over 7 towers	— COM. TYROL — TRANS(S)Y(I)L		(1100-06)
Augsburg	Austrian arms	— BUR. COM. TYR.	A	(1107)

1035   TALER 1712-1718 (VIENNA)
CAROL vi D. G. RO: IMP. S: A: GER: HISP. - HU. BO. REX., bust R in beaded border.
.ARCHIDVX. AVSTRIAE. DVX. BVRG. COM. TYROL. date, crowned double eagle with arms
on breast.
Some differences in the face. The 1712 has large VI. The 1717 has BVR.

1036   TALER 1716, 1719, 1721, 1722 (VIENNA)
CAROL: VI. D:G:R:I: - S:A: GE: HI: HU: BO: REX., bust R.
ARCHID: AUST: DUX. .BU: COM: TYROL: date, crowned double eagle with arms.
The eagle's tail on the 1722 differs.

1037   TALER 1720. 1722-1735 (VIENNA)
Similar to #1036 with changed armor and decoration at neck.
Similar to #1036 with some punctuation changes.
Varieties of the 1733 with BV. and BVR.

1038   TALER 1735-1740 (VIENNA)
Similar to #1036 with changed armor and neck decoration.
Similar to #1036.

1039   TALER 1713, 1718 (GRAZ)
CAROL. VI. D:G: RO: IMP: S:A: GER: HISP: - HV: ET BO: REX., bust R in half a
   beaded border.
.ARCHIDVX AVSTRIAE. DVX. BVRG: ET STYRIAE. EC. date., crowned double eagle with
   arms on breast.
I have not seen the 1718.

1040   TALER 1723, 1728, 1729 (GRAZ)
CAROL. VI. D:G:R:I: - S:A: GE: HI: HV: BO: REX., bust R.
Similar to #1039.
The dates differ from one another in many details. Larger letters on 1728.
I have not seen the 1729.

1041   TALER 1732 (GRAZ)
CAR. VI. D:G.R.I.S.A. - GE. HI. HU. BO. REX:., bust R with changed armor and drapery.
:ARCHID: AUST: DUX: - :BUR: ET: STYRIAE: 1732;, crowned double eagle with arms.

1042   TALER 1735, 1737, 1738 (GRAZ)
CAR: VI: D:G:R:I:. - S:A: GE: HI: HU: BO: REX:, bust R with changed armor and drapery.
Similar to #1041.
The 1735 has AVST.

1043   TALER 1740 (GRAZ)
Similar to #1042.
ARCHID: AUST. DU - X: BUR: ET: STYRIAE. 17 - 40:, double eagle as above.

1044   3 TALERS 1713 (ST. VEIT)

1045   2 TALERS 1713 (ST. VEIT)

1046   TALER 1713 (ST. VEIT)
 CAROLVS: VI. D:G. ROM. IMP. S.A. GERM. HISP. HVNG. BOH. REX., bust R in double circle.
 ARCHIDVX: AVSTRIAE: ET CARINTHIAE decoration 17: - :13:, crowned double eagle with arms on breast.

1047   TALER 1713 (ST. VEIT)
 Similar to #1046, another bust in more nearly complete circle.
 ARCHIDVX: AVSTRIAE. & CARINTHIAE. 17 - 13, crowned double eagle with arms.

1048   TALER 1714 (ST. VEIT)
 CAROLUS. VI. D:G: ROM: IMP: S:A: GERM: - HISP: HUN: BO: REX., another bust R.
 .ARCHIDUX AUSTRIAE - .ET CARINTHIAE. 1714., crowned double eagle with arms.

049   2 TALERS N.D. (HALL)

CAROLUS. VI. D:G: RO: IMP: S:A:G:H:H:B: REX., bust R.
ARCHIDVX. AUSTRIAE. DVX. BURGUNDIAE. COM: TYR., crowned double eagle with arms.

050   TALER 1713 (HALL)

CAROLVS. VI. D:G: ROM: IMP: SE: A:G: - HIS. HV: BO: REX., bust R.
ARCHIDUX. AVSTRIAE. DUX. BVRG: COM: TYROL: 17 - 13., crowned double eagle with
  arms.

051   TALER 1714, 1716, 1718 (HALL)

CAROLUS. VI. D:G: ROM: IMP: S:A:G: HI: HU: B: REX, bust R.
ARCHIDUX. AVSTRIAE. DUX. BVRG. COM: TYROLIS. date, eagle as above.
A 1715 has been reported.

A. A 1714 with obverse of #1050.

1052   2 TALERS 1719 (HALL)

1053   TALER 1719, 1721, 1724, 1725, 1734 (HALL)
Similar to #1051, slightly changed robes on bust.
ARCHID: AUST: DUX. - BU: COM: TYROL: date, eagle similar to above with tail to rim.
The 1734 has changed punctuation and a different tail to eagle on reverse.

1054   TALER 1724, 1725, 1727-1729, 1732, 1734 (HALL)
CAROL. VI. D.G.R.I.S.A. - GE. HI. HU. BO. REX., bust with larger head R.
Similar to #1053, shape of shield and eagle's tail changed.
The 1724 has AVST. DVX. Many slight variations over the years.

1054A   TALER   1729
Similar to #1054 with much thinner bust.
Similar to #1054 with differently shaped shield.

1055   TALER   1730, 1733,   1736-1738   (HALL)

Similar to #1054, handsomer bust.
Similar to #1054.

1056   TALER   1737   (HALL)

CAROL. VI. D.G.R.I.S. - .A. GE. HI. HU. BO. REX, bust R with number below.
Similar to #1055, different punctuation and another tail on eagle.
The numerals found under the bust are 1, 2, 3, 4, or 5.

1057   TALER   1712   (KREMNITZ)

CAR: VI. D:G:R:I:S: arms A:G: - arms HI: HU: B: REX., bust R.
.ARCHID: AVS: D: BU: - M. MOR: CO: TY: 1712, crowned double eagle with arms.
   K - B below.

1058   TALER 1715 (KREMNITZ)
Similar to #1057 with changed bust.
Similar to #1057 with date 1715.

1059   TALER 1718-1719, 1721-1730 (KREMNITZ)
Similar to #1057 with HV. and new bust with low neck.
ARCHID. AV. D. BV. - M. MOR. CO. TY. date, double eagle with arms. K - B below.
The 1717 and 1720 have been reported.

1060   TALER 1730-1735 (KREMNITZ)
Arms CAR: VI. D:G:R:I: - S:A:G: HI: H:B: REX. Arms, new bust R.
ARCHID: AU: D: BU: M. - MOR: COM: TY: date, crowned double eagle, arms, with K - B
below.

1061   2 TALERS 1740 (KREMNITZ)
1062   TALER 1736-1740 (KREMNITZ)
Similar to #1060 with new bust R.
Similar to #1060.

1063   TALER 1712, 1715 (PRESSBURG)
CAROLUS. VI arms D:G.R.I.S.A. GER. HISP. HUN arms BOH: REX, bust R in circle with
I.G.S. below.
ARCHID. AV. DV. BV - MAR. MOR. CO. TY. divided date., crowned double eagle with arms
on breast, C - H below, and PW under all in cartouche.

1064   TALER 1717-1718 (PRESSBURG)
CAROLVS. VI arms D:G:R. IMP: S:A: GER: HI arms HUNG: BOH, bust R in half beaded
circle.
DAL: CRO: SCLAV: REX: ARCHID: AVST: D: BVRGVN: date, crowned double eagle with
arms. C - H and P - W below.

1065   TALER   1711 (PRAGUE)

CAROL' vi D.G. RO. IMP. S.A. GER. HIS. - HU. BO. REX., bust R.
ARCHID. AUST. DUX. BURG. ET. SILE. MAR. MOR. 1711., crowned double eagle with
four part arms on breast.

1066   TALER   1712 (PRAGUE)

CAROLUS. VI: D:G: - .ROM: IMPER - .SEMP: AU., bust R.
GERM: HISPA: HUN: ET - BOHEMIAE. REX. 1712, crowned double eagle with Bohemian
arms on breast. I.A.P below.

1067   TALER   1712 (PRAGUE)

CAROLUS. VI: D.G. - .ROM: IMPER: - SEMP. AV., larger bust with smaller head R.
GERM: HISPA: HUNG: ET - BOHEMIAE. REX: 171Z., arms and initials similar to preced

068   TALER 1713 (PRAGUE)

CAROLUS. VI. D :G: R :I :S :A : GER : HISP: HUN: BOH : REX, bust R.
ARCHID : AUST : D: BURG: ET SILES: MARG: MOR. 17 - 13., crowned double eagle with
four part arms on breast.

069   TALER 1713-1714 (PRAGUE)

CAROLUS. VI. D:G:R:I:S:A: GER: HISP - HU: BO: REX, bust R with I.G.R. in drapery.
ARCHID: AUST: D: BURG: & SILES: MAR: MOR. divided date., crowned double eagle with
four part arms on breast.

TALER 1715-1716 (PRAGUE)

CAROL. vi D.G. RO. IMP. S.A. GER. HIS - HU. BO. REX., bust R in beaded circle.
.ARCHID. AVST. DUX. BURG. ET. SIL. MAR. MOR. date., eagle and arms.

C

1071   TALER 1716-1717 (PRAGUE)

Similar to #1070, another bust without beaded border.
Similar to #1070 with SILE.

1072   TALER 1717 (PRAGUE)

CAROL: VI: D:G:R:I: - S:A: GE: HI: HU: BO: REX.*, bust R.
.ARCHI. DAVST. DUX. BURG. ET. SILE MAR. MOR. 1717.* , eagle and arms.

1073   TALER 1717 (PRAGUE)

Similar to #1072, another bust, and no star after legend.
Same as #1072.

1074   MINING TALER 1717 (PRAGUE)

Same as #1073.

.S. IOACHIMBSTHALISCHE AUSBEUT THALER. 1717., crowned double eagle with arms of
Bohemia and St. Joachim.

1075   TALER 1718 (PRAGUE)

CAROL vi D.G. RO. IMP. S.A. GER. HIS. - HU BO REX, bust R.

.ARCHID. AUST. DUX. BURG. ET. SILE. MAR. MOR.1718., eagle and arms.

A. There is another bust with wider Order Band over the shoulder.

1076   TALER 1718 (PRAGUE)

Similar to #1075 with smaller bust and head.

Similar to #1075.

1077   MINING TALER 1718 (PRAGUE)

CAROL vi D.G.R.I. - S.A.G. HIS. H.B. REX., bust R.
.S. IOACHIMBS-THALISCHE AUSBEUT THALER.1718., crowned double eagle with arms of
Bohemia and St. Joachim.

1078   TALER 1718-1719 (PRAGUE)

Same as #1077.
.ARCHID. AUST. DUX. BURG. ET. SILE. MAR. M. date., eagle and arms.

1079   TALER 1719 (PRAGUE)

CAR, vi D.G.R.I.S.A.G. - HI. HV. B. REX., bust R.
ARCHID. AV. D. BV. - M. MOR. CO. TY. 1719, eagle and arms.

1080 **TALER 1719-1720 (PRAGUE)**
Similar to #1079 but bare head R.
Similar to #1079.

1081 **TALER 1721, 1722, 1724 (PRAGUE)**
Similar to #1079 with another bust.
Similar to #1079 with new tail on eagle and monogram FS below.
The three dates differ from one another in details of face and drapery.

1082 **TALER 1723 (PRAGUE)**
CAROL: VI. D:G.R.I.S.A. - G. HI. H.B. REX., bust with low neck R.
ARCHID. AV. D. BVRG. - M. MOR. CO. TY. 1723, eagle and arms with monogram FS.

1083   TALER 1725 (PRAGUE)
CAR, vi D.G.R.I.S.A.G. - HI. HV. BO. REX, shorter bust R.
Similar to #1081 with date 1725.

1084   TALER 1726-1727 (PRAGUE)
CAROL: VI: D:G:R:I: - S:A: GE: HI: H: B: REX., new bust R.
ARCHID: AUST: DUX. - BU: COM: TYROL: date, eagle, arms, and monogram.

1085   TALER 1727-1728 (PRAGUE)
CAROL: VI: D:G:R:I: - S:A: GE: HI: HU: B: REX., bust R.
Similar to #1084 with new tail on eagle and no monogram.

1086 TALER 1728-1732, 1735-1736, 1739-1740 (PRAGUE)

CAROL: VI: D:G:R:I: - S:A. G(E): H(I): H: BOH: REX., bust R.
Similar to #1085.
1728,29,39,40 have G:H:H:BOH: A 1739 has GE:H:H:BOH:
1730,31,35,36 have GE:HI:H:BOH:
Only the 1735-36 have a curl over the left shoulder. The 1736 also comes without the curl.

1087 TALER 1736-1740 (PRAGUE)

CAR: VI. D:G:R:I: - S:A:G: H(I): H(U): BOH: REX., bust R, with curl over left shoulder
on 1736-1738 and no curl on 1738-1740.
Similar to #1085.
1736 has G:H:H: 1737,38,39 have G:HI:H: 1740 has G:HI:HU:
1736,37,38 are divided I:-S;   1738,39,40 have S:-A: A 1740 has A:-G:

1088 TALER 1712 (KUTTENBERG)

CAROLUS: VI: D:G: - ROM: IMPER. - SEMP. AV., bust R.
GERM: HISP: HUNG: ET - .BOHEMIAE, REX. 171Z., eagle with Bohemian lion, arms and
B - W below.
A 1715 has been reported.

1089   TALER 1713 (BRESLAU)

CAROL, VI: D:G: RO: IMP: S:A: GE: HIS:- HU: BO. REX, bust R.
ARCHIDVX. AVSTRIAE. DVX. BVR. &. SIL. 1713 in band, crowned double eagle with arms.

1090   TALER 1714 (BRESLAU)

CAROL, VI. DG. RO: IMP: S.A. GE: HIS. - HU: BOHE. REX., bust R.
ARCHIDUX. AVSTRIAE. DVX. BVR. &. SILE: 1714 in band, eagle and arms.
Varieties with large and small armholes.

1091   TALER 1715 (BRESLAU)

CAROL, (:) VI. D.G. RO. IMP: S.A. GE: HIS: HU: BOHE: REX, bust R.
ARCHIDUX. AVSTRIAE. DVX. BVR(.) &(.) SILE. 1715, eagle and arms with no band.
Two varieties differing in hair arrangement and punctuation.

1092   TALER   1716-1717   (BRESLAU)

CAROL, VI. D :G. - .R.I.S.A.G. HI. H.B. REX., bust R.
ARCHIDVX. AVSTRIAE. DVX. BVR. &. SILE. date, eagle and arms.
Three varieties of each date. A 1716 with SILES.

1093   TALER   1717-1718   (BRESLAU)

Similar to #1092, changed bust and punctuation.
ARCHIDVX: AVSTRIAE: DVX. BVR. &. SILES: date, eagle with small tail and arms.

1094   TALER   1718   (BRESLAU)

CAROL. VI: D:G.R.I. - .S.A. GE: HI: H: BO: REX., new bust R.
ARCHID: AUS: DUX. - .BUR. &. SILESIAE :1718, eagle and arms.

1095   2 TALERS 1722 (BRESLAU)

1096   TALER 1719-1722 (BRESLAU)
CAROL. VI: D:G: - :R.I.S.A.G. HI. H. B. REX., bust R.
ARCHID. AVST. DVX: - :BVR. &. SILESIAE: date °, eagle and arms.
The four dates differ in harness, Order Chain, and tail of eagle.
The 1721 has double haloes on the eagle.

1097   2 TALERS 1723, 1725, 1732 (BRESLAU)

1098   TALER 1723-1732, 1736, 1738-1740 (BRESLAU)
CAROL: VI. D:G:R:I:S:A: - GE. HI. HU: BO: REX., new bust R.
ARCHID: AUST: DUX. - BUR & SILESIAE: date., eagle and arms.
Numerous small differences. The armor on the sleeve differs from 1738 on.
I have not seen the 1736.

1099   TALER 1713 (BRIEG)
CAROLUS. vi. D.G. ROM. IMP. S.A. GER: HIS: H & BO: REX., bust R in beaded circle,
MONETA. NOVA. ARGENTE - METALLI. FOD. REICHSTEIN. 17 - 13, crowned double eagle
with arms. C - B and crossed pickaxes below.

1100   TALER 1712 (SIEBENBÜRGEN)
CAROLVS VI. D.G.R. IMP. S.A. GERM. HISP. HVNG. BOH. REX., bust R in rope border.
ARCHIDVX AVSTR. D.B. MAR. MOR. COM. TYROL. 1712., crowned double eagle with two
part arms in rope border.

1101   TALER 1713, 1715 (SIEBENBÜRGEN)
CAROL, vi D:G: RO. IMP. S.A. GER: HIS - .HV. BO. REX., new bust R in rope border.
ARCHIDVX. AVST: DVX. BVRG. PRINC. TRANSSYL: date, eagle and arms.

1102   TALER 1715 (SIEBENBÜRGEN)
CAR. vi. D:G:R:I:S:A: GER. - HI: HV: B: REX., new bust R, no border.
Similar to #1101 with AVS:T:

1103   TALER 1721, 1722, 1724, 1734 (SIEBENBÜRGEN)

CAR. VI. (:) D:G:R:I:S:A(:) - G(:) HI: HV:B: REX, bust with low neck R.
ARCHID: AV: D: BV: PR. - INC. TRANSYL: date, eagle and arms.
The busts on the four dates differ from one another. The 1724, 1734 have the division S:A:G:
  - HI: and the 1721, 1724 PRI - NC. The 1724 has HV. BO.; the 1734 H: B.; the 1721
TRANSSIL. There is a curl over the left shoulder on the 1734.

1104   TALER 1736-1738, 1740 (SIEBENBÜRGEN)

CAROL: VI. D:G:R:I: - S:A: GE: HI: H: B: REX.. new bust R.
ARCHID: AU: D: BU: PR - INC: TRANSYL: date., eagle and arms.
A variety of the 1736 has the division PRI - NC.
I have not seen the 1740.

1105   TALER 1738 (SIEBENBÜRGEN)

1106   TALER 1739 (SIEBENBÜRGEN)

CAROL: VI. D:G:R:I: - S:A: GE: HI: HU: BO: REX., bust R.
ARCHID: AUST: D: BUR: - PRIN: TRANSYL. 1739, eagle and arms.

1107   TALER 1713-1714 (AUGSBURG)

CAROL. VI D.G. ROM - IMP. S.A.G.H.H.B. REX., bust R.

ARCHIDUX.,AUSTRIAE. - DUX. BUR. COM. TYR. date., crowned double eagle with Habsburg arms on breast. Below two horseshoes and A.

The hair arrangement and the robes on the two dates differ. There are three varieties of the 1713. A. With robes like 1714. B. With no period after 1713. C. With triangle after REX and horseshoes higher.

For other issues of Charles VI see Milan, Mantua, Naples, Sicily and Austrian Netherlands.

MARIA THERESIA   1740-1780

	Arms	Reverse legend	Initials	Numbers
Vienna	Austrian arms	— BURG. CO(M). TYR.	I.C.-S.K.	(1109-17)
			I.C.-F.A.	
			I.K.-S.C.	
Graz	lion	— BURG. & STYR.		(1118-19)
Hall	eagle	— BU(RG). CO(M). TYR.	A - S	(1120-24)
	Austrian arms		V.C.-S.	
Kremnitz	madonna and	— PATRONA HUNG.	K.B. or K	(1125-34)
	child reverse		EVM - D	
			S.K.-P.D.	
Nagybanya				(1135)
Prague	lion	— BURG. SI. M. MO.	EvS - A.S.	(1136-40)
	Austrian arms	— BURG. CO. TYR.	EvS - I.K.	
	2 part	— AUSBEUTH		
Siebenbürgen or	bird over 7 towers	— LO. B.M.D. ETR.		
Karlsburg		— TRAN. CO. TY.	AH - GS	(1141-46)
Günsburg	Austrian arms	— BURG. CO. TYR.	G	(1147-51)
		— BURGOVIAE		

1109   TALER 1741-1744 (VIENNA)
MAR: THERESIA. - D:G: REG: HUNG: BOH:, bust R.
ARCHID: AUST: DUX - BURG: COM: TYR: date, crowned arms in elaborate frame.
There is a klippe of the 1743.

1110   TALER 1744-1745 (VIENNA)
MAR. THERESIA - D.G. REG. HUNG. BOH., smaller bust R.
Similar to #1109, crowned arms supported by griffins, sprays below.

1111   TALER 1746-1752 (VIENNA)

M. THERESIA. D.G. - R. IMP. GE. HU. BO. REG., bust R.
ARCHID. AUST. DUX - BURG. COM. TYR. date., crowned double eagle with arms.
The eagle's tails differ. Some dates without final periods. An X after 1751-1752.
I have not seen the 1748.

1112   TALER 1753-1765 (VIENNA)

Similar to #1111, armored bust R.
Similar to #1111 except CO. and date X.
Slight changes in dress, eagle's tail, arms over the years. Two varieties in eagle's tails on
1756 and 1758.

1113   MINING TALER 1758, 1765 (VIENNA)

Same as #1112.
S. ANNAE FUND GRUBEN - AUSB. THA. IN. N. OE. date X, crowned double eagle with
two part arms, crossed pickaxes below.
The two dates differ in many details.

1114   TALER 1765-1767 (VIENNA)

M. THERESIA. D:G. - R. IMP. HU. BO. REG., veiled bust R.
Similar to #1112 with simpler arms double crowned.
The 1765-1766 come with A under bust; the 1766-1767 without.
The 1765-1766 have no initials on reverse; the 1766-1767 have I.C.-S.K.

1115   TALER 1767-1771 (VIENNA)

Similar to #1114, differently veiled bust R.
Similar to #1114, with I.C. - S.K. below eagle's wings.
A variety of the 1767 with initials I.K. - S.C.

1116   TALER 1772-1779 (VIENNA)

Similar to #1114, smaller veil on bust R.
Similar to #1114, with I.C. - S.K. or I.C. - F.A.
1772-1774 with I.C. - S.K. 1774-1779 with I.C. - F.A. The 1774 has large and small I.C. - F

1117   TALER 1780 (VIENNA)
Similar to #1116 with larger bust R.
Similar to #1116 with I.C. - F.A.

1.18   TALER 1765 (GRAZ)
M. THERESIA D :G.R. - IMP. GE. HU. BO. REG   gown R.
ARCHID. AUST. DUX - BURG. &. STYR.   e eagle and arms.

➋   TALER 1765 (GRAZ)
Similar to #1118, bust in armor R.
Same as #1118.

D

1120   TALER 1749-1751, 1753-1754, 1763-1765 (HALL)

M. THERESIA. D:G.R. - IMP. GE. HU. BO. REG., bust in decorated gown R.
ARCHID. AUST. DUX - BU(RG). COM. TYR. date. X, crowned double eagle with arms.
Many varieties. No X after date on 1749-1750. Division D:G. - R. IMP. on 1749-1751. BURG. on
1749-1750 and BURG. CO. on 1764-1765. A 1754 with REG*. A 1764 with smaller eagle's wings.

1121   TALER 1751-1753, 1755-1765 (HALL)

Similar to #1120 but bust with plain gown.
ARCHID. AUST. DUX. - BU. COM. TYR. date X, eagle and arms.
A 1755 with REG*. 1763-1764 with smaller lettering.

1122   TALER 1751-1752, 1764-1765 (HALL)

Similar to #1120 but bust with armor R.
Similar to #1121.
Some varieties especially in the 1765. The 1764 has BURG. CO. A 1765 has the division D:G. - R

123   TALER 1765-1772 (HALL)

M. THERESIA. D:G. - R. IMP. HU. BO. REG., veiled bust R.
ARCHID. AUST. DUX - BURG. CO. TYR. date.X., eagle with simpler arms doubly crowned.
Initials A.S. on obverse 1765-1768, on reverse 1769-1772. a.S. on the 1765, 1766, 1768. A.S. from
1766 on. A 1765 witn F. for A.S.
I have not seen 1767, 1769, 1770.

124   TALER 1773-1776 (HALL)

Similar to #1123, bust with smaller veil R.
Similar to #1123.
A.-S. on 1773-1774. V.C.-S. on 1774-1776.

1125   TALER 1741-1742 (KREMNITZ)

MA. THERESIA. - D:G: REG: HUN: BO:, bust R.
S: MARIA MATER DEI — PATRONA HUNG: date, madonna and child in rays, shield below,
K - B at sides.
Varieties of both dates with spelling on obverse MAR. and HUNG.

1126   TALER   1743-1744   (KREMNITZ)
M: THERES: - D:G: REG: HU: BO., bust R.
Similar to #1125.
The 1743 comes with one curl or two, the 1744 with one.

1127   TALER   1744   (KREMNITZ)
Similar to #1126, changed and older bust with O below.
Similar to #1126.

1128   TALER   1744-1745   (KREMNITZ)
Similar to #1126 with changed bust and smaller head.
Similar to #1126.

1129 TALER 1746-1748 (KREMNITZ)

M: THER: D:G:R: - I:G:H:B:R:A:A:D:B:C:T:, bust R.
Similar to #1128.
I have not seen the 1748.

1130 TALER 1749-1752 (KREMNITZ)

Same as #1129.
Similar to #1129 with new and larger shield under madonna.

1131 TALER 1751-1752 (KREMNITZ)

M. THER. D:G.R. IMP. - GE. HU. BO. R.A.A.D.B.C.T., bust R.
Similar to #1130 with X after date.

1132   TALER 1752-1765 (KREMNITZ)
Similar to #1131 with armored bust R.
S: MARIA. MATER. DEI. - PATRONA. HUNG. date.X, madonna and child on rayed star
background, small K - B below.
The initials are different size in different positions. A new pattern of rays with 1758. Two
varieties of 1753, 1760, 1763.

1133   TALER 1767-1773, 1775-1780 (KREMNITZ)
M. THER. D.G.R. IMP. - HU. BO. R.A.A.D.B.C.T., crowned arms supported by two angels,
sprays below.
S. MARIA. MATER. DEI. - PATRONA. HUNG. date X, seated madonna and child with K
or B below and initials EVM - D. or S.K. - P.D.
K on 1767-1776. B on 1777-1780. EVM - D on 1767-1773. SK - PD on 1775-1780. The size of the
lettering differs. New cloud and drapery arrangement with 1775 on. Variety of 1767 with
no EVM - D.
I have not seen the 1773.

1134   TALER 1780 (KREMNITZ)
M. THERESIA. D.G. - R. IMP. HU. BO REG., large bust R with B below.
ARCHID. AUST. DUX. - BURG. CO. TYR. 1780.X., crowned double eagle with arms and initials
S.K. - P.D. below.

1135   TALER   1763   (NAGYBANYA)
Mont. #1213.

1136   TALER   1746,   1748-1755,   1757,   1759-1761   (PRAGUE)
M. THERESIA. D.G. - R. IMP. GE. HU. BO. REG., bust R.
ARCHID. AUST. DUX. - BU(RG), SI(.) M. MO. date, crowned double eagle with arms.
Three patterns of dress decoration. BURG. on 1746-1750, BU. on others. An X after dates 1751 on.
I have not seen 1752, 1761. A 1742 is reported.

1137   MINING TALER   1758-1759   (PRAGUE)
Similar to #1136, bust with different dress and hair arrangement.
S. IOCHIMS. THALER - AUSBEUTH date X, crowned double eagle with two part arms on breast, crossed hammers below.
The two dates differ in many details.

1138   TALER   1769-1772   (PRAGUE)

M. THERESIA. D.G. - R. IMP. HU. BO. REG, veiled bust R.
ARCHID. AUST. DUX. - BURG. CO. TYR.date.X, crowned double eagle with arms, E v S
A.S. below.
I have seen only the 1771.

1139   TALER   1773-1775   (PRAGUE)

Similar to #1138 with REG., bust with narrow veil R.
Similar to #1138.
1773 with E v S. - A.S. 1774-1775 with E v S - I.K.

1140   TALER   1780   (PRAGUE)

Similar to #1139 with larger bust R.
Similar to #1138 with AVST.
With initials A. E v S. - I.K. or B. P.S. - I.K.

141   TALER 1742 (SIEBENBÜRGEN)

MAR: THERESIA - D:G: REG: HUNG: BO:, bust R.
ARCH: A:D: BU. PR: TRAN: - N:D: LO: B:M:D: ETR: 1742, crowned arms in fancy frame.

142   TALER 1743-1744 (SIEBENBÜRGEN)

MAR: THERESIA. - D:G: REG: HUNG: BO, new bust R.
Similar to #1141 with changed frames for the arms.
The frames on the two dates differ. The 1743 has fruit clusters under the griffins instead of the leaf sprays on the 1744.

143   TALER 1745 (SIEBENBÜRGEN)

MAR. THERESIA - D:G. REG. HUNG. BOH., smaller bust R.
Similar to #1141 with changed punctuation and a new frame for arms.

1144   TALER 1747, 1749-1750 (KARLSBURG)
M. THERESIA. D :G. - R. IMP. GE. HU. BO. REG., bust R.
ARC. AU. DUX. BU. MEDI. - PR. TRAN. CO. TY. date, crowned double eagle with arms.
The tail of the eagle on the 1750 differs.

1145   TALER 1751-1762, 1765 (KARLSBURG)
Similar to #1144 with armored bust R.
AR. AU. DUX. BU. ME. PR. - TRAN. CO. TY. date.X, eagle and arms.
There are many variations. The tails differ with a larger one on 1751 than on the later dates.
The 1758, 1760, 1762 have RE. for REG. The 1765 has TYR. for TY. A variety of the 176?
has the division R. - IMP. and HV :

1146   TALER 1780 (KARLSBURG)
M. THERESIA. D.G. - R. IMP. HU. BO. REG., veiled bust R.
ARCHID. AVST. DUX. - BURG. CO. TYR. 1780.X, double eagle and arms with A.H. - G.S
below.
There are large and small sets of initials.

147   TALER 1764-1765 (GÜNSBURG)
Similar to #1145 with D :G: and armored bust R.
ARCHID. AUST. DUX - BURG. CO. TYR. date.X, crowned double eagle with arms on breast
and G in circle below.
The drapery differs slightly on the two dates. A variety of the 1765 with S.C. under the bust.

148   TALER 1766-1767 (GÜNSBURG)
M. THERESIA. D.G. - R. IMP. HU. BO. REG., crowned and supported two part arms with
sprays and S: C: below.
ARCHID. AUST. D. BURG. - MARGGR. BURGOVIAE.X, in a wreath AD / NORMAM
CONVENT. / date.
Varieties of the 1766 with no S :C: under arms, and with no period after CONVENT or date.

149   TALER 1765, 1767-1772 (GÜNSBURG)
M. THERESIA. D:G. - R. IMP. HU. BO. REG., veiled bust R with S:C: below.
ARCHID. AUST. DUX - BURG. CO. TYR. date.X, crowned double eagle with simpler arms.
The 1765 has two busts both differing somewhat from the later dates. Variety with no initials
below bust.

1150   TALER   1773-1777   (GÜNSBURG)
Similar to #1149 with D.G. and bust with narrower veil R.
Similar to #1149 with DUX.
The 1773-1774 have S.C. under the bust; the 1775-1777 have S.F.

1151   TALER   1780   (GÜNSBURG)
Similar to #1150 with new bust R.
Similar to #1150.
There are 5 varieties. A. With S.F. B. With S.F. and small ST under bust. C. With F.S. D. With
TS- IF on reverse. E. With P.S. - I.F. on reverse.

For other issues of Maria Theresia see Milan and the Austrian Netherlands.

FRANCIS I, HOLY ROMAN EMPEROR   1745-1765

ienna   W - I; I.Z.V.; G.T.K.; A.W.
Iall   H - A
Kremnitz   K - B
Prague   P - R
Karlsburg   C - A

152   TALER 1746-1747, 1749-1751 (VIENNA)
FRANC. D.G RO. I.S. - A. GE. IER. R. LO. B.M.H.D., bust R.
IN TE DOMINE - SPERAVI date., crowned eagle with arms on breast separating W - I below.
The eagle's tail differs on almost all dates, as do the size and placing of the W - I. The 1751
has .X after the date.

153   TALER 1748, 1753, 1756 (VIENNA)
Similar to #1152 with R.I.S. and the second type bust.
Similar to #1152 with .X after the date.
There is no X after 1748.

154   TALER 1761, 1763-1765 (VIENNA)
Similar to #1153 with older bust and I.Z.V. below.
IN. TE. DOMINE. - SPERAVI.date.X, arms similar to #1152.
A. Variety of 1761 with G.T.K. B. Variety of 1764 with A.W.

1155   TALER 1749-1751, 1753-1757, 1759-1765 (HALL)

FRANC. D:G.R.I.S.A. - GE. IER. R.LO.B.M.H.D., bust R.
Similar to #1153 with H - A.
The 1753 and 1763 have the second type bust (#1153). No .X after date on 1749-1750. Som
mantles are flowered and some plain. Smaller bust with 1753 on. The eagle's tail differs o
1756-1757 and 1763 and a differently shaped shield on the last two. I have not seen the 176

1156   TALER 1746-1748, 1750 (KREMNITZ)

Similar to #1152.
Similar to #1152 with SPERAVI. date and K - B.

1157   TALER 1751-1765 (KREMNITZ)

Legend similar to #1155 with second bust (#1153)
Similar to #1154 with K - B.
The portrait was sharpened after 1755 and on some dates the mantle is decorated. The eagle
tail differs, and on many dates the K - B is above the tail. I have not seen the 1765.

¶158   TALER 1746-1749, 1751-1752, 1757 (PRAGUE)
FRANC. D:G.RO.I.S.A. - GE. IER. R.LO.B.M.H.D., bust R.
Similar to #1156 with P - R.
The 1751-1757 have date X. I have not seen the 1748 or 1752.

¶159   TALER 1753-1755, 1757, 1759-1762 (PRAGUE)
Similar to #1153.
Similar to #1153 with P - R.
The 1754, 1759-1761 have dots in the armor and chain mail on the breast. The 1761-1762 have
P-R above the eagle's claws.

160   TALER 1747-1751, 1753, 1758 (KARLSBURG)
FRANC. D.G.RO.I.S.A. - G. IER. R.LO.B.M.H.D., bust R.
Similar to #1152 with no . after the date and C - A.
Slight changes in the bust on 1749-1751. The 1753 has the second bust (#1153) with GE. and X
after the date. I have not seen the 1751 or 1758.

For other issues of Francis I see Tuscany and the Austrian Netherlands

JOSEPH II, HOLY ROMAN EMPEROR   1765-1790

Vienna   I.C.-S.K.; I.C.-F.A.; A.
Hall   a-S; A-S; V.C.-S.; F
Kremnitz   B
Prague   EvS-A.S.; EvS-I.K.; C
Günsburg   S.-C.; H

1161   TALER 1765-1767, 1769-1772 (VIENNA)
IOSEPH: II. D:G:R:I:S:A: - COR. & HER. R.H.B. &c., bust R with A below.
ARCH. AUST. D. BURG. - LOTH. M.D. HET. date. X, crowned double eagle with arms on breast separating initials below.
No initials on 1765-1767 ; I.C. - S.K. on 1766-1767, 1769-1772.

1162   ORDENSTALER 1768-1769 (VIENNA)
Similar to #1161, another bust with Order band across shoulder.
Similar to #1161 with I.C. - S.K.
The two dates differ in many details.

1163   TALER 1773-1776, 1778-1780 (VIENNA)
Similar to #1161, older, shorter bust with A below.
Similar to #1161.
Some changes from 1775 on in the portrait and in the eagle's tail.
No A on 1773-1774. On reverse I.C. - S.K. on 1773-1774 ; I.C. - F.A. on 1774-1780.

164 TALER 1765-1767, 1771, 1775-1777 (HALL)

Similar to #1161, slightly changed bust with F below.
Similar to #1161 with different initials.
1765, 1767 with a S; 1765-1767, 1771 with A-S; 1775-1777 with V.C.-S.

1165 TALER 1770-1775 (PRAGUE)

Similar to #1164 with C below bust.
Similar to #1161 with other initials.
1770-1773 with EvS-A.S.; 1774-1775 with EvS-I. K. I have not seen the 1771-1772.

1166 TALER 1766-1769, 1771 (GÜNSBURG)

Similar to #1164 with H below bust.
Similar to #1161 with S.- C.

E

AS HABSBURG RULER ALSO 1780-1790

1167   TALER 1781-1782, 1784-1790 (VIENNA)
IOSEPH. II D.G.R.I.S.A. - GERM. HV. BO. REX., head R with A below.
Similar to #1161 with no initials.
The Medici arms are altered slightly with 1785. The 1787-1790 come with no curls under bust
The 1785 comes with and without A.

1168   TALER 1781-1783, 1785 (VIENNA, KREMNITZ)
IOS. II. D.G.R.I(MP). S.A. - G.H.B.R(EX). A.A.D.B. ET(&). L., two angels holding crown
over Hungarian arms with sprays below.
S. MARIA MATER DEI - PATRONA HUNG. date.X., madonna and child, mintmark in frame
below.
A on Vienna 1783, 1785; B on Kremnitz 1781-1783.
The Vienna pieces have I./IMP., R./REX., and ET/&. Kremnitz have the second reading.

1169   TALER 1785-1786, 1789 (VIENNA, KREMNITZ)
IOS. II. D. - G.R. IMP. S.A. - G.H.B. REX. A. - A.D.B.&.L., similar to #1168 but all details
altered.
Similar to #1168.
A on Vienna all dates; B on Kremnitz 1786.

170   KRONENTALER   1783-1784, 1788-1790   (VIENNA, KREMNITZ)

IOSEPH. II. D.G.R.I.S.A. GER. HIE. HVN. BOH. REX., head R with mm. below.
ARCH. AVST. DVX. BVRG. LOTH. BRAB. COM. FLAN. date., three crowns in angles of
Burgundian cross.
A on Vienna all dates ; B on Kremnitz 1784, 1788.

For other issues of Joseph II see Milan and the Austrian Netherlands.

LEOPOLD II   1790-1792
AS KING OF HUNGARY AND BOHEMIA

1171   TALER 1790

LEOPOLDVS II. D.G. HUNGAR. BOHEM. GALLIC. LODOM. REX., head R with A below.
ARCHIDVX AVST DVX BVRG. ET LOTH. MAG. DVX. HETR. 1790 X, three crowns over
arms supported by griffins.

1172   TALER 1790

LEOP. II. D. - G. HU. BO. GA. LOD. - REX. A.A.D.B. ET. L. _ M.D. HETR., crown supported by two angels over Hungarian arms, branches below.
S. MARIA MATER DEI - PATRONA HVNG. 1790. X, madonna and child, A in frame below.

AS HOLY ROMAN EMPEROR

1173 TALER 1790-1792
LEOPOLDVS II. D.G.R. IMP. S.A. GERM. HV. BO. REX., head R with A below.
ARCH. AVST D. BVRG. - LOTH. M.D. HET. date. X, crowned double eagle with arms or breast.

1174 TALER 1790-1791
LEOP. II. D. - G.R. IMP. S.A. G.E. - HV. BO. REX. A.A.D. - B.L.M.D.H., crown supported by two angels over Hungarian arms, sprays below.
Similar to #1172.

1175 KRONENTALER 1790-1792
LEOPOLD. II. D.G.R.I.S.A. GER. HIE. HVN. BOH. REX., bust R with A or H below.
ARCH. AVST. DVX. BVRG. LOTH. BRAB. COM. FLAN. date ., three crowns between arms of Burgundian cross.
A - Vienna 1790; H - Günzburg 1791-1792.

For other issues of Leopold II see Milan and Tuscany.

FRANCIS II 1792-1835
AS KING OF HUNGARY AND BOHEMIA

1176 TALER 1792
FRANCISCVS. D.G. HVNGAR. BOHEM. GALLIC. LODOM. REX., head R with A below.
ARCHIDVX AVST. DVX. BVRG. ET LOTH. MAG. DVX HETR. 1792. X, three crowns over arms supported by griffins.

1177 TALER 1792
FRANC. D. - G. HV. BO. GA. LOD. - REX. A.A.D.B. ET L. - M.D. HETR., crown supported by two angels over Hungarian arms, sprays below.
S. MARIA MATER DEI - PATRONA HVNG. 1792. X, madonna and child, A in frame below.

AS HOLY ROMAN EMPEROR

1178 [3] TALER 1792-1800
FRANCISCVS. II. D.G.R. IMP. S.A. GERM. HV. BO. REX., head R with A below.
ARCH. AVST. D. BVRG. - LOTH. M.D. HET. date. X, crowned double eagle with arms on breast.

1179   TALER   1792

FRANC. II. - D.G.R. IMP. S.A. GE. - HV. BO. REX. A.A.D. - B.L.M.D.H., crown supported
by two angels over Hungarian arms, sprays below.
Similar to #1177.

1180   KRONENTALER   1792-1798

FRANC. II. D.G.R.I.S.A. GER. HIE. HVN. BOH. REX., head R with mm. below.
ARCH. AVST. DVX. BVRG. LOTH. BRAB. COM. FLAN. date., three crowns in angles of
Burgundian cross.
A—Vienna 1792-1798; B—Kremnitz 1793-1797; C—Prague 1795-1797; E—Karlsburg 1797; F—
Hall 1795-1797; G—Nagybanya 1797; H—Günsburg 1793-1797.

For other issues of Francis II see Milan and the Austrian Netherlands.

AUERSPERG

THIS noble Austrian family, already known in the 11th century, originated from Auersperg, south of Laibach in Carniola.

In 1653 Johann Weikard (1615-1677), the powerful cabinet minister of Ferdinand II and tutor of Ferdinand IV, was granted the rank of prince of the empire together with the county of Wels and the dukedom of Münsterberg in Silesia. In 1664 he obtained he lordship of Thengen and in 1671 complete ownership of his native county, Gottschee. Münsterberg was sold to Prussia in 1791. In 1811 Thengen and other lands were ransferred to Baden.

HEINRICH   1713-1783

1181   TALER 1762

HENRICVS S:R:I: PRINCEPS AVRSPERG DVX MINSTERBER, bust R with A. WIDEMAN below.

COM. IN THENG: S.C.M. INTIM: CONS: ET SVPR: STABULI PRAEFECT: 1762, crowned and mantled arms.

Records of 260 minted at Vienna.

BATTHYANI

THIS old Hungarian family, originating from Kovagoors, were made hereditary counts of Nemet-Ujvar (Gussing).

Count Karl Joseph, in 1764, after fifty years of distinguished service, was granted the title of prince of the empire and the coinage right. The name of Strattman on the coins of his great nephew Ludwig came from his grandmother's side.

KARL JOSEPH   1764-1772

1182   TALER 1764

CAROL. S:R:I: PRINC: DE. BATTHYAN. P: I:N: U: &.S: COM: AUR: U: E: C:C:P:S:U: S:C:, bust R with I.TODA.F. on sleeve.

GEN: C: MAR: U:L: DIM: COL: U:S:C: & R:A:M:A:I: CONS: &.S: CONF;M; 1764, crowned, mantled, and supported arms.

4000 minted.

1183   TALER 1768

CAROL. S:R:I: PRINC: DE.BATTHYAN: P:I:N:U. &.S: - COM: AUR. V.ET. ORD. S:STEPH
R:A. MAGN: CRUC.EQUES. C:C.P.S. VS:C:, bust R with I.TODA.F. on sleeve.
GEN: C: MAR: U:L: DIM: COL: U:S:C: &. R:A:M:A:I: CONS. &. S: CONF:M: 1768, crowne(
and mantled arms.
300 minted, apparently in 1770.

LUDWIG   1788-1806

1184   TALER 1788

LVDOVICVS S.R.I. PRINCEPS DE BATTHYAN STRATTMANN., head R with I.N.WIRT.
below.
PERPETVVS IN NEMET VIVAR S.C.R.A.M. ACT. CAM. INC. COM. CAST. PERP. ET
SVPR. COM. 1788., crowned, mantled. and supported arms.

COLLOREDO-MANNSFELD

THE family of Colloredo descended from the Swabian lords of Waldsee, after whose extinction it was confirmed in all their titles and privileges. It appears that the family came from Friaul, where it obtained from Poppo von Aquileja (1019-45) the lordship and castle of Mels north of Udine. In 1302 they built a new castle near the village of Colloredo. While several branches of the family distinguished themselves in Imperial service, only the Weikard line appears in numismatic history. This branch came into Austria and Bohemia in 1693 from their native Italian place as heirs to the extinguished Asquinian line, acquiring among others the lordship of Opocno. In 1724 the brothers Hieronimus and Rudolf were granted the titles of counts of the Empire. The son of Hieronimus, Rudolf, the Vice Kanzler of the Empire, received in 1763 the title of prince and the coinage right, which he never exercised.

His son, Franz Gundacker married Maria Isabella, heiress of the counts and princes of Mansfeld-Fondi, and by Imperial decree combined the latter's titles and name with his own, thus becoming prince of Colloredo-Mannsfeld.

FRANZ GUNDACKER   1788-1807

1185   TALER 1794

FRANC. GVND. S.R.I.P. COLLOREDO. MANNSFELD. C. IN. WALDS. V. C. IN. MELS. M. IN. S. SOPH. S.R.I. PRO. CANC., crowned and mantled arms.

BEY GOTT IST RATH - UND THAT, St. George killing dragon, 1794 below.

This "Motto" taler is apparently known only as a restrike.

DIETRICHSTEIN

THE well known house of Dietrichstein which presented to Austria many spiritual and worldly lords was of old Carinthian descent with its original place near Feldkirchen in Carinthia, not far from the present Dietrichstein castle. Since the 12th century it was in the service of the bishops of Bamberg, to whose Carinthian possessions Feldkirchen belonged.

Pankraz von Dietrichstein (died 1508) obtained from Maximilian I the title of hereditary cup-bearer in Carinthia. That heraldic symbol appears in the later family arms. His sons Franz (died 1550) and Siegmund (died 1533) founded the two branches of the house which later obtained coinage rights; the county branch of Pulsgau and the princely line of Nikolsburg.

Sigismund Ludwig (died 1678) of the Pulsgau branch, court official of Middle Austria, obtained from Ferdinand III for himself and his male descendants the coinage right. He was followed by his son Sigismund Helfried (died 1698), and the last member of this line, his grandson Karl Ludwig, nephew of Sigismund Helfried. The Nikolsburg branch did not strike any coins in the 18th century.

KARL LUDWIG   1698-1732

1186   TALER 1726

CAR: LUD: S.R.I. COM: - A DIETRICHSTAIN, bust R.
LIBER BARO IN - HOLLENBURG. 1726, crowned arms in elaborate frame.
500 minted in Vienna.

ESZTERHAZY

THE Eszterhazys were probably the richest and most famous Hungarian noble
family. Already prominent in the 12th century, they were divided into the Zerhazy
and Illeshazy branches.

Franz Zerhazy, who inherited the lordship and castle of Galantha in Slovakia near
Pressburg, named himself Eszterhazy in 1584. In 1687 Paul Eszterhazy, hereditary
count of Forchenstein (Frakno), was granted the title of prince of the empire by
Leopold I. Nikolas Joseph, who like other members of his family held the highest
offices and titles in Hungary, was the only Eszterhazy to exercise the coinage privilege.

NIKOLAS JOSEPH   1762-1790

1187   TALER 1770

NICOL. S.R.I. PRINC. ESZTERHAZY DE GALANTHA PERP. COM. IN FRAK., bust R.
US. C. &. R.A.M. CONS. INT. GEN. C. MAR. &. NOB. PRAET. H. TURMAE CAPIT. 1770.,
crowned and mantled arms.
406 minted in Vienna.

KHEVENHÜLLER - METSCH

THE Khevenhüller family, originally from Bamberg, settled in Carinthia in the 15th century. In the first half of the 16th century, it divided into two main branches, Aichelberg-Frankenburg and Hohen-Osterwitz. During the anti-reformation wars many members left their native land, but the family regained power when Ehrenreich (died 1675) returned to Austria and obtained the title of count of the empire in 1673.

His son Sigismund Friedrich held high offices in the Empire and was followed by his son Johann Joseph, who was granted the title of prince in 1763. The latter married Karoline, daughter of Johann Adolf Metsch, and after the extinction of the Metsch male heirs, by the Emperor's permission, he combined his father-in-law's name and titles with his own, thus becoming count and later prince of Khevenhüller-Metsch.

JOHANN JOSEPH   1742-1776

1188   TALER 1761
> IO. IOS. S.R.I. COM. A. KEVENHVLLER METSCH IN OSTERWIZ, bust R with S PRINS on sleeve.
> AVR: VELL. EQV: S.S.C.C.R.R.MM. ACT. INT. ET. CONFERENT. CONSIL. ET SVPR. CAMER. 1761, helmeted and supported arms.

1189   TALER 1771
> IO. IOS. KEVENHULLER AB AICHELBERG S.R.I. PR. A. METSCH, bust R with A.W. below.
> A.V.&. O.S. STEPH. R.A.M.C. EQ. U.S.C.R. - A.M.A.I. CONS CONF. M.&. S.A. PRAEF. 1771, crowned and mantled arms in double chain.
> 200 minted in Vienna.

LOBKOWITZ

THIS Bohemian family, already noted in the 15th century, reached its greatest importance during the 17th.

Ladislaus II of the Popel-Lobkowitz branch obtained from Maximilian II the lordship of Neustadt in Oberpfalz on the Waldnab. His son, Zdenko Adalbert, (died 1628), kanzler of the Bohemian kingdom, was a staunch defender of the imperial and Catholic causes. Although his possessions were expropriated during the successes of the Bohemian States, after the victories of Ferdinand II he was granted the title of prince for his long and faithful service. His lordship was raised into a principality and named Sternstein.

His son Wenzel Eusebius (died 1677) served three emperors in high offices and in 1646 obtained from Ferdinand III the Silesian principality of Sagan. In 1675 he fell into disfavor with Leopold I, who revoked his titles and confiscated his estates. However, after his death his son Ferdinand August Leopold (died 1715) again gained imperial favor.

Franz Josef Maximilian, the great-grandson of Ferdinand August Leopold, was the only member of the family in whose name actual coins were struck, although some showtalers and medals had been previously coined. He was a great lover of music and patron of Beethoven. His carefree life in Vienna and on his Bohemian estate, combined with the financial crisis of that time and unlucky theatrical direction, led him into bankruptcy in 1813.

The coins of 1794 were struck under the regency of his mother, Gabriele of Savoy-Carignan, and his cousin, August von Lobkowitz.

FRANZ JOSEF MAXIMILIAN   1784-1816

1190   TALER 1794

> FR. IOS. MAX. PR. DE. LOBK. DVX. RAVD. PR. COM. IN. STERNST., bust R with VI below.
> TVT. MAR. GAB. PR. VID. DE. LOBK. NAT. PR. SAB. CAR. ET AVG. PR. DE. LOBK.
> 1794., two shields crowned and mantled.
> 300 minted in Vienna.

NOSTITZ-RIENECK

THE noble family of Nostitz was of Slavic descent and spread out from Lausitz during the late 14th century.

Only the Nostitz-Rieneck line, whose founder Johann Hartwig (died 1683), court councillor in Bohemia, was made a count of the Empire in 1651, is of numismatic interest. In 1673 he obtained from the elector of Mainz the Franconian county of Rieneck. He died in 1683 during the Turkish siege. The coins of the Nostitz family were struck in one year only by his youngest son Anton Johann, chamberlain of the Bohemian kingdom and burggraf of Eger. He died without male heirs.

ANTON JOHANN   1683-1736

1191   TALER 1719

ANTONI, IOH. S.R.I. COM. DE NOST: ET RIN., bust R.
S.C.M. CONS. INT: CAM: SVPR. R. BOH. PRAEF. BVRGG. EGR, crowned and supported
arms on base with GFN. and 17 - 19. below.
Nuremberg mint.

ORSINI-ROSENBERG

THE princes of Orsini-Rosenberg were of Carinthian descent, and contrary to some
opinions, had no relationship with the Bohemian family of Rosenberg, which ended
in 1614. Also, the officially acknowledged lineage with the Roman Ursini or Orsini
family, from whom the Rosenbergs in Bohemia were supposed to derive, is very
doubtful.

Johann Andreas, burggraf in Carinthia, in 1648 was made a count of the Empire.
His son Wolfgang Andreas (died 1695), after some quick documentary proceedings, in
1684 obtained the right to call himself "Ursini and Rosenberg." His grandson Wolfgang
Franz Xaver, according to some contemporaries, could have played a very important
political role if he had had as much ambition as he had talent. His successful career
began under Maria Theresia and continued under her successors. He held many important positions of trust and confidence and was raised to the rank of prince in 1790. It
appears that the grant of the prince's title did not mention any coinage rights, and no
coins were struck during his lifetime. The history of the pieces struck later in the
19th century is somewhat confusing.

FRANZ URSINI   1794-1832

1192   TALER 1793

FRANCISCVS. VRSIN. S.R.I. PRINCEPS. ROSENBERG., head R with I.N. WIRT.F. below.
MONETA. NOVA. AD. NORMAM. CONVENTIONIS.1793., crowned, mantled, and supported
arms.
Apparently struck in 1853.

PAAR

THE Paar family, of Italian descent, was known in Austria from the 16th century
It played the same role in Austrian postal history as the Thurn and Taxis family
did in the Empire proper. For almost 300 years and thru many generations, the family
was in charge of postal management in Austria, Hungary, Bohemia, and at the imperial
court in Vienna. This hereditary arrangement lasted until the nationalization and
reorganization of the Austrian postal system.

In 1636 the head of the family was created a count of the Empire, and in 1769
Joseph II granted to Johann Wenzel the title of prince. It is said that his personal
services, such as escorting both wives of the Emperor to Vienna and his assistance in
promoting the marriages of the Emperor's two sisters, rendered some help in obtaining
his title. Johann Wenzel was followed by his son Wenzel, well known art lover, drafts-
man, and etcher, who was the second and last member of the family to strike coins.

JOHANN WENZEL   1769-1792

1193   TALER 1771

> IOH. WEN. S.R. IMP. PRINCEPS A. PAAR., bust R.
> S.I. AUL. REG. HER. &. P.   GE. H. POST. MAG.1771., crowned double eagle with arms on
> breast.
> 200 minted in Vienna in 1771 edge with laurels; 500 (dated 1771) minted in 1781 with lettered
> edge CANDIDE ET FELECITER

WENZEL   1792-1812

1194   TALER 1794

> WENCESLAVS. S. ROM. IMP. PRINCEPS. A. PAAR., head R with I.N.WIRT.F. below.
> SVP. IMP. AVL. REG. HER. - P. G. HER. POST. MAG.1794., eagle and arms similar to
> preceding.
> 250 minted in Vienna.

SCHLICK

THE Schlick family's rise into the nobility was partly the result of some falsified documents. Kasper (died 1449) was the chancellor of three emperors and obtained coinage rights in 1438 and the title of count. His nephew Kasper II, founder of the Schlackewerth line, received permission to call himself count of Passaun and Weisskirchen. Passaun (Passan, Bassano) was a county in upper Italy near Treviso. Those titles appear on the coins of Schlick. His four sons, following the example of Archduke Sigismund of Tyrol and the dukes of Saxony, started in 1517 the coinage of dollar-size silver. Coins from the silver of their mines in Joachimsthal, Bohemia, were first nicknamed "Joachimsthaler," later abbreviated into thaler, from which our word "dollar" is derived. It is interesting that while the west adopted the ending of Joachimsthaler, the Russians took the first part of it. The denomination "Yefimok" comes from Yefim, which is Joachim in Russian.

During the first part of the 16th century the Schlicks considerably increased their holdings in Bohemia and Hungary, but during the Schmalkald (Reformation) war they joined the opponents of the emperor, who after the victory of Muhlberg in 1547 confiscated most of their possessions including Joachimsthal.

By the beginning of the 17th century the family had returned to power, and Kasper II's great-grandson, Heinrich (died 1650), fieldmarshal and high office holder under Ferdinand II and Ferdinand III, opened a mint in the county of Plan. This was continued by his son, Franz Ernst (died 1675). In 1665, however, he had to sell Plan to settle his father's debts. His successors, Franz Joseph (son), Franz Heinrich (nephew of Franz Joseph), and Leopold Heinrich (Franz Heinrich's son) were imperial office holders in Bohemia and had their coins struck at the Prague mint.

FRANZ JOSEPH   1675-1740

1195   TALER 1716

FRANC. IOS. SCHLICK. COM. A BASSAN.& WEISK., Holy Family above, crowned arms separating 17 - 16.

CAROL. vi D.G. ROM. IMP. _ S.A. GER. HISP. HU. B. REX., crowned double eagle with arms on breast, F. S. below.

2112 minted at Prague.

FRANZ HEINRICH 1740-1766

1196 TALER 1759

FRANC: HEN: SCHLIK: S:R:I:C: DE PASSANO: &. WEISKIRCHEN., des   gene
similar to #1195 with date 17 - 59

M. THERESIA. D.G.R. - IMP. GE. HU. BO. REG., crowned double eagle with arms   ow

LEOPOLD HEINRICH 1766-1770

1197 TALER 1767

LEOPOL: HEN: SCHLIK: S:R:I:C: DE. PASSANN: &. WEISKIRCHEN, design si
#1195 with 17 - 67.

Similar to #1196 with no GE. and with X after legend and new crown and arms.
below.

SPRINZENSTEIN

THE barons and counts of Sprinzenstein descended from the Florentine scientist and humanitarian Paulo Riccio (died c. 1541), who was councillor to Ferdinand I and in 1529 obtained from the bishop of Passau the lordship of Sprinzenstein in Upper Austria near Rohrbach. In 1530 he was elevated to the rank of hereditary freiherr.

His son Hieronimus (died 1570) obtained the lordship of Neuhaus. The descendants of his eldest son in 1646 were made counts of the Empire, and one of them, Ferdinand Max (died 1679), councillor of Ferdinand III and high office holder under Leopold I, received the coinage right. Ferdinand Max died without sons, and the only coins of Sprinzenstein were struck at the Augsburg mint by his nephew Franz Ignaz and the latter's nephew Johann Ehrenreich, both of whom had high official positions.

FRANZ IGNAZ   1639-1705

1198   TALER 1705

FRANC. IGNAT. S.R.I.C. &. DOM. DE ET IN SPRINZENSTEIN ET NEUHAUS *, bust R. ARCHI. MONETARIVS HAEREDITARI, VTRIVSQ. AVSTRIAE *1705*. helmeted arms with pinecone and horseshoes for the Augsburg mint.

JOHANN EHRENREICH   1705-1729

1199   TALER 1717

IOAN. ERNRICUS S.R.I.C.& DOM. DE ET IN SPRINZENSTEIN ET NEUHAUS*, bust R. ARCHI. MONETARI,. HAEREDITARI, UTRIUSQ: ARCHIDUCAT. AUSTRIAE*1717*, helmeted arms with Augsburg mintmarks as above.

TRAUTSON

THE Trautson family belonged to the Tyrolian nobility and by the middle of the 15th century possessed the hereditary landmarshal's office in that territory. In 1598 the lordship of Falkenstein, the family's holding in northern Austria near the Moravian border, was elevated into a hereditary county.

The numismatic history of the family began with freiherr (free baron) Paul Sixtus (died 1621), high court official of Rudolf II. In 1600 he fell into the emperor's disfavor, but returned to power under the imperial successors, and his countship and coinage rights were confirmed by Matthias. Under Ferdinand II he was the governor of a section of Lower Austria.

Paul Sixtus got into difficulties over irregularities in his coining operations, but was able to continue through the emperor's favor. He was followed by his son, Johann Franz (died 1663), governor and land-marshal of Lower Austria. The coinage of Trautson was suspended in 1639 but resumed again by his two sons Franz Eusebius and Johann Leopold Donat, two officials of the emperor.

FRANZ EUSEBIUS   1663-1728

1200   TALER 1708, 1715
> FRANC. EUSEB. TRAVTHSON COM. IN FALKHENSTAIN, bust R.
> .L.B. IN SPRECHEN: ET - SCHROVENSTEIN., helmeted arms dividing date with MM below.

JOHANN LEOPOLD   1663-1724

1201   TALER 1719
> IO. LEOP. S.R.I. PRINCEPS TRAVTSON. COM. IN. FALKENSTEIN, bust R.
> AVR. VELL. EQV. S.C.& CAT. MAI. INTIM. - & CONFERENT. CONSILIAR.1719, helmeted crowned, and mantled arms.

WINDISCH-GRÄTZ

THE counts of Windisch-Grätz originated from Grätz in Wendishen and descended
from the counts of Weimar. They already had possessions in Styria at the beginning
of the 15th century. After a number of family divisions they obtained the title of freiherr (free baron) in 1551, and in 1565 the title of "Hereditary Stable Master" of Styria,
which appears on their later coins.

From the oldest branch, the Erasmian line, Gottlieb (died 1695) was elevated by
Leopold I to the rank of count of the Empire. Gottlieb's son, Leopold Viktorin Johann,
diplomat and statesman, received from Karl VI in 1730 the coinage right. The first of
his family to strike coins, he was followed by his grandson, Joseph Niklas, court official
and scientist, who also struck coins but no talers.

LEOPOLD VIKTORIN JOHANN   1727-1746

1202   TALER 1732

LEOPOLD. VICT. IO. S.R.I. COMES. A. WINDISCHGRATZ., bust R with B below.
S.C.M. CONS. STATUS. INT & HAERED. PER. STYR. SUP. STAB. PRAEFECTUS 1-7-3-2,
helmeted and supported arms.

BRIXEN

THE bishopric of Brixen (Italian Bressanone), established in 992 was located in the Austrian Tyrol, bordering on the Venetian Republic. In 1027 the bishops acquired considerable temporal power, and in 1179 received minting privileges. In 1802 the bishopric was assigned to Austria and in 1803 united with the Tyrol.

CASPAR IGNATZ, COUNT VON KÜNIGL (1702-1747)

1203   TALER 1710

CASPARVS IGNATIVS D. G. EPISCOP,.. bust R with Augsburg mm. below.
ET S. R. I. PRINCE - PS BRIXINENSIS ° 17 - 10°, two shields in frame crowned and capped.

SEDE VACANTE   1778-1779

1204   2 TALERS 1779

CAPITVLVM / BRIXINENSE / REGNANS SEDE / VACANTE. / 1779. in center, star above, 15 shields around.
AD NORMAM CONVENTIONIS. - V. EINE FEINE MARCK, eagle in center with INSIGNIA CAPITULI BRIXINENSIS. above.

OLMÜTZ

OLMÜTZ, the Czech Olomouc, the eventual capital of Moravia, was made the see of a wandering bishopric in 1063. Although the mint right had been conferred on the bishopric by 1141, it was not until the 17th century, after the bishops had become princes of the Empire, that there was any coinage of consequence. In 1777 the bishop was raised to the rank of an archbishop.

KARL III. DUKE OF LORRAINE   1695-1711

1205   TALER 1701

D.G. CAROLVs: - ◊ - EPVS: OLOMVCEN, bust R.
DVX. LOTHAR & BAR. - S.R.I. PCP. S.R.C.B. COM., crowned arms with 17 - 01 in crown.

1206   TALER 1702

D:G: CAROLvs. - EPVS: OLOMVCE:, bust R.
DVX. LOTHAR: ET. BAR. S:R.I.PS.R.C. BO: COM. 1702, crowned and supported arms.

1207   TALER 1703
D:G: CAROLVS. EPISCOPVS. OLOMVCENSIS:*:, bust R in beaded border.
DVX. LOTHAR: ET. BAR: S:R:I:PS:R:CA:BO: COMES.1703, crowned and supported arm
in beaded border.
SR 3651 reports a similar taler dated 1706 with U's for V's on the obverse and on the reverse
DUX .... PS.RE.CA.BO.CO: 1706.

1208   TALER 1704
DEI GRATIA CAROLVS EPISCOPVS OLOMVCENSIS+, bust R in beaded border.
DVX LOTHAR: ET BAR: - S:R:I:PC - PS:RE:CA:BO:CO: 1704, crowned and supported
arms in beaded border.

1209   TALER 1705
Same legend as #1208, U's for V's, ornament, bust R in beaded border.
DUX. LOTHAR: ET BAR: - S:R:I: - PCPS: RE:CA:BO:CO: 17 - 05, crowned and supported
arms in beaded border.

211   **TALER 1706-1707**
Same legend as #1209 with ; ('06) or no ornamentation ('07), bust R in border.
DUX LOTHAR. ET BAR. - S:R:I:P S. RE.CA.BO. CO(M). date ;, crowned and supported
arms in border.
The busts and the shape of the shields differ on the two dates. There are two dies for each
side of the 1706.

1212   **TALER 1709-1710**
D:G: CAROLUS EPISCOPUS OLOMUCENSIS., bust R in beaded border.
DUX LOTHAR. ET BAR. - S:R:I: - PS. R:C:B: COM:, date, crowned and supported arms
in border.
The 1710 is 1709 altered.

1213   **TALER 1711**
Same legend as #1208 with *, bust R in border.
Legend like #1208 but COM. 17 - 11, crowned and supported arms in border.

For other issues of Duke Karl see Osnabrück 1698- and Trier 1711-

WOLFGANG, COUNT VON SCHRATTENBACH 1711-1738

1214 TALER 1712
WOLFFGANGVS D:G: EPVS. OLOMVCENSIS DVX: S:R:I: PRCEPS*, bust R in beaded border.
REG. CAP. BO. ET DE SCHRATTENBACH COMES 1712 ; crowned and mitred arms in border.

1215 TALER 1713-1714
WOLFFGANG, D:G:S:R:E: CARD: DE SCHRATTEMBACH EP: OLOM:, capped bust R in beaded border.
DVX S:R:I: PCPS. REG. - CAP. BOHEM. COMES: date divided with *, hatted, mitred, and crowned arms in border.
After he became a cardinal.

1216 TALER 1716
WOLFFG: D:G:S:R:E: PRESB: CARD. DE SCHRATTEMBACH EP. OLOM., capped bust R.
DVX S:R:I:PS:R:C:B: COM. CON. - GER. S:C:R:M: CON. IN ET ACTV. 1716, hatted, mitred, and crowned arms.

1217   2 TALERS 1722
1218   TALER 1718-1722, 1724-1725
WOLFFG. D:G:S:R:E: PRESB. CARD. DE SCHRATTEMBACH EP. OL(O)(M)., capped
bust R.
DVX S:R:I:P:R:C:B: COM. CON. GER. S:C:R:M: CON. IN ET AC(TV) (AL), hatted, mitred,
and crowned arms separating date.
Although these coins are generally alike, each has its own portrait, differing in details with
a different frame for the coat of arms.
Individual features of obverse and reverse: 1718 OL+/ACTV+ or Actv+; 1719 D: for DE and
OL+/AC:; 1720 SCHRATEMBACH and OLOM./ACTV.; 1721 OLOM./ACTV:; 1722 OLOM*/
ACTVAL.; 1724 2 var. OLO. or OLO*/ACTVAL. or ACTVal.; 1725 2 var. in busts
OLO./ACTVAL.

1219   TALER 1726-1727
WOLFFG: D:G:S:R:E: PRESB: CARD: D: SCHRATTEMBACH: EP: OL*, bust R.
DVX S:R:I:P:R:C:B:C: PROTEC. - GER. S:C:R:M: CON. IN. ET AC., three coats of arms
dividing date below capped, mitred, and crowned.
These differ slightly and there are two varieties of each date.
A. 1726 wtih E. OL* and S.C.M. B. 1727 with some periods for colons on the obverse.

1220   TALER 1728
Similar to #1219 but with SCHRATTENBACH EP: OL: DVX* and older bust.
S:R:I:PS:R:C:B:C: PROTEC. GER. S:C:R:M: CON. IN. ET ACTVAL. 17 - 28., three arms,
hatted, mitred, and crowned.

1221 TALER 1729

WOLF. D:G:S:R:E: PRESB. CARD. D: SCHRATTENBACH E: O: DVX, capped bust R.
Legend like #1220 but ends ACTV*, three arms dividing date above 1-7-2-9.

1222 TALER 1730

WOLF. D:G:S:R:E:P: CAR. D - SCHRATTENBACH EP. OL., St. Wenzeslaus seated on a
cloud between two angels, two shields below.
S: CYRILL. PRIM. APOST. MORAV.1730, saint seated to L, book with IHS, arms at R.

1223 TALER 1730, 1733-1735

WOLFFG: D:G:S:R:E: PRESB: CARD: D: SCHRATTENBACH. EP: OLO: DVX*, capped
bust R.
S:R:I:PS:R:C:B:C: PROT. GER: S:C: - R:M: CON IN. ET ACTVAL + date, three arms,
hatted, mitred, and crowned.
The 1730 differs in portrait, DUX, and reverse division S:C:R: - M:CON.

224 TALER 1731

Legend similar to #1223 with WOLF: and DVX., bust R.
S.R.I.PS:R:C:B:C: PROT. GER: S`- C:R:M: CON. IN. ET ACTVAL. 17-31, three arms, hatted, mitred, and crowned.

225 TALER 1736

Similar to #1223 with JD under bust.
Similar to #1224 with ACTVAL + and divided date.

226 TALER 1736-1738

Similar to #1225 with DVX.
Similar to #1225 with S:C: _ :R:M: and undivided date.
The 1737 has two slightly differing portraits. The 1738 has WOLF: . . . PR: . . . EPVS: OLO: DVX.

JACOB ERNST, COUNT VON LIECHTENSTEIN   1738-1745

1227   TALER 1739-1740
IAC: ERN: D:G: EPUS: OLOMUCENSIS: DUX. S:R:I: PCPS., bust R.
REG: CAP: BO: ET: DE: LIECHTENSTEIN COMES date, mitred and crowned arms.

1228   TALER 1741
IAC: ERN: D:G: EPVS. OLOMVCENSIS DVX S:R:I:, bust R.
PCPS: REG: CAP: BO: ET. DE. LIECHTENSTEIN COMES, 1741 above, mitred and crowned
arms.
A. Variety with JD under bust.

1229   TALER 1742
IAC: ERN: D:G: EPVS: OLOMVC: DVX. S:R:I:SPCP., bust R.
REG: CAP: BO: ET: DE. LIECHTENSTEIN COMES, mitred and crowned arms dividing
17 - 42 at sides.

230   TALER   1742-1745

Similar to #1229 except that legend ends PCPS.
Similar to #1229 except larger frame and date divided at ends of legend.
The 1742 has the same incorrect obverse legend ending SPCP as #1229.

FERDINAND JULIUS, COUNT VON TROYER   1745-1758

232   TALER   1752, 1756

FERD. IUL. D.G.S.R.E. CARDIN. DE TROYER., bust R with D.
EPISC. OLOM. DUX. S.R.I. PRINC. RÉG. CAP. BOH. COM, hatted, mitred, and crowned
    arms dividing date.
SR#3679 lists a 1746 which seems to have disappeared.

ANTON THEODOR, COUNT VON COLLOREDO-WALDSEE   1777-1811

233   TALER   1779

ANT. THEODOR. D.G. PRIM. A. EP. OLOMU. DUX., bust R with W below.
S.R.I. PR. RE. CAP. BOH. & A COLLOREDO & WALD. CO:1779;*, capped arms with
    I.C. - F.A. at sides.

SALZBURG

SALZBURG, located between modern Austria and Bavaria, has been the site of a city since pre-Roman times. The Roman trading town Juvavum was burned in 477 and the modern city grew up around the monastery founded there about 700 by St Rupert of Worms, at the invitation of Duke Theodo of Bavaria. St. Rupert becam the patron saint of the foundation, which grew until it incorporated most of th valley of the Salzach river. St. Boniface made it a bishopric in 739 and Pope Leo III an archbishopric in 798. The name, inspired by the extensive salt deposits in the region had become attached to it by 816.

Its possessions continued to increase and its archbishop was created a prince of th Empire in 1278 by Rudolf of Habsburg. The bishoprics of Freising, Ratisbon, Brixen Gurk, Chiemsee, Seckau, and Lavant all became suffragan, and Salzburg's influenc was powerful in Renaissance times. The cathedral, which is modeled on St. Peter's was constructed from 1614-1668, and the university was founded by Archbishop Coun Paris von Lodron in 1623.

The princebishops, often somewhat bigoted and usually drawn from noble Bavarial and Austrian families, seem rarely to have been on good terms with their subjects. I the Catholic counter-reformation Salzburg became a center of militant Catholicism The Jews were exiled about 1500. The great expulsion of the Protestants came unde Leopold Anton, Count von Firmian (1727-1744). Late in 1731 between 20,000 and 30,00 were expelled or emigrated; King Friedrich Wilhelm I of Prussia aided some 17,00 of them to settle in his country.

In 1750 the archbishop became primate of Germany and shared with Austria th pre-eminence in the college of princes. Under Hieronymus, Prince von Colloredo (1772-1803), the archbishopric was probably the richest principality in the souther half of the Empire. After the Peace of Luneville in 1802 the archbishopric was secu larized and transformed into an electorate principality of some 250,000 people for th Grand Duke Ferdinand III of Tuscany.

JOHANN ERNST, COUNT THUN HOHENSTEIN 1687-1709

1234   TALER 1701-1709

IO. ERNEST. D:G: - ARCHIEP: SA(L): S:A:L: Within border SVB TVVM PRAE - SIDIVM CONFV - G. Madonna and child over arms.
S: RUDBERTUS. - EPS. SALISBURG: däte, saint standing over arms.
Many varieties.

FRANZ ANTON, PRINCE VON HARRACH   1709-1727

235   TALER 1709
FRANC: ANTO: D:G: ARCHI: ET PR: SALISB: S:S:A:L: PR: DE HAR:, arms.
ANNO / DNI MDCCIX / ET / REGIMINIS / PRIMO / F.F. in wreath.

236   TALER 1709, 1711
FRANC: ANTO: D:G: - ARCH: PR: SAL: S:A:L:, similar to #1234 with different arms.
S: RVDBERTUS: - EP: SALISBVRG. date, similar to #1234.

237   TALER 1710-1712, 1714-1720
FRANCIS(C)(VS) ANTO(N). S.R.I. PRINC. DE HARRACH, bust R.
D.G. ARCHIEPISCOP & S.R.I. PRINC. SALISBURG. S.S.A.L. date, arms.
Many varieties. The 1716-1717 come with and without * under the bust.

1238   TALER 1712, 1714-1718, 1722

FRANC: ANTO(N): D:G. - ARCHI: PR: SAL. S.A.L., madonna and child over arms.
S: RUDBERTUS. - EPS: SALISB: date., saint seated L with arms.

1239   TALER 1723-1727

FRANC: ANT: S:R:I: - PRINC: AB HARRACH., bust R.
Similar to #1237.
G under bust 1723-1724, 1727 ; nothing or B on 1725 ; D on 1726.

LEOPOLD ANTON ELEUTHERIUS, FREIHERR VON FIRMIAN   1727-1744

1240   TALER 1728

LEOPOLDUS. D.G. - ARCH. ET. PRINCEPS, bust R with B below.
SALISBURG. S. SED. APOS. LEGAT. GERM. PRIM. divided date, arms.

241 TALER 1728-1735

LEOPOLDUS. D:G: - ARCHI: PR: SAL. S:A:L., madonna and child over arms.
Similar to #1238.
The 1735 has SALISB.

1242 TALER 1738-1740, 1742, 1744

Similar to #1240 smaller bust capped with F.M.K below and unbroken legend.
Similar to #1240.

JACOB ERNST, COUNT VON LIECHTENSTEIN 1745-1747

1243 TALER 1745

IACOBUS ERNEST: D:G. ARCH & PRINC: SALIS: S:A:L:, madonna and child beside small arms.
S: RUPERTUS EPISCOP: SALISBURGENS: date, saint seated on cloud.

1244   TALER   1746

IACOBUS ERN: D:G. ARCH. ET. PRINCEPS, bust R with F M K below.
Similar to #1240 with new arms and shape of shield.

ANDREAS JACOB, COUNT VON DIETRICHSTEIN   1747-1753

1245   TALER   1748, 1750

ANDREAS. D.G. ARCH. ET. PRINCEPS, bust R with .FM.K. below.
Similar to #1240 with new arms and shape of shield.

1246   TALER   1752

ANDREAS. D.G. ARCH. ET. PRINCEPS. SALISB: S.A.L., madonna and child standing beside
small arms.
S. RUPERTUS. EPISCOP. SALISBURGENS:1752., saint seated looking R with arms.

SIGISMUND III, COUNT VON SCHRATTENBACH 1753-1771

1247   TALER 1753-1756, 1758, 1761

SIGISMUNDUS. D:G: ARCHIEPISCOP(US), bust R.
S.R.I. PR: SALISB: S.S. AP. LEG: NAT: GER: PRIMAS divided date, arms.
The base under the shield varies.

1248   TALER 1754

SIGISMUND. D:G: A & PR: SAL: S:A:L: NAT: GERM: PRIMAS, motto on band, madonna
and child in square, arms on R.
Similar to #1246 with date 1754.

1249   TALER 1757

SIGISMUNDUS. D:G.A. EPISC. & PR. SALISBURG., bust R with P.M. below.
S. AP. S. LEG. NATUS. GERM. PRIMAS.1757., saint seated to R; in exergue S. RUDBERTUS.
E.S.
F.M. on or below the bust.

1250   TALER 1758

Similar to #1248.
Legend like #1246 with date 1758, saint standing facing L.

1251   TALER 1759

SIGISMUNDUS. D:G: ARCHIEPISCOP:, bust R with M.K. below.
Legend like #1246 with date 1759, saint seated on cloud.

1252   TALER 1759

SIGISMUND: D:G. A & PR. SAL. S.A.L. NAT. GERM. PRIMAS *, two arms.
Similar to #1251.

1253 TALER 1759-1760

SIGISMUNDUS. D:G:A.&.P.S.A.S.L.N.G.P., bust R.
Legend like #1246, seated saint with small madonna.
The 1759 with no initials or MK - FM.

1254 TALER 1761-1762

SIGISMUND(US). D.G. A & PR. SA(L). S.A.L. NA(T). GER. PRIM(AS)., bust R.
Similar to #1253.
The 1761 has two different decorations on the robe.

1255 TALER 1761

SIGISMUNDUS. D:G.A. EPISC. & PR. SALISBURG, bust R.
S.A.S. LEG. NATUS GERM. PRIMAS.1761 *, two arms.

1256   TALER   1761

Similar to #1251.

S.R.I. PR. SALISB. S.S.AP. LEG. NAT. GER. PRIMAS 17 ✻ 61, two arms.

1257   TALER   1762-1764

SIGISMUND. D:G.A. & PR. SAL., bust R with (F)MK below.

S.A.S. LEG. NATUS. GERM. PRIMAS(.) date, two arms crowned and mantled.

A number of busts with different arrangement of the robes and position of the cross on breast.

1258   TALER   1765

SIGM.D:G.A. & P.S.A.S.L.N.G. PRIM., bust R.

Crowned and mantled arms with 17 - 65 above.

259   TALER 1761, 1765-1769

SIGM. D:G.A. & P.S.A.S.L.N.G. PRIM., bust R.
Crowned and mantled arms with date below.
Much variation in composition and spacing with wide or close dates.
Varieties of 1765: small or large date; with F.M or F.M.K below bust.
Varieties of 1766: F.M. below bust.
The 1767-1769 have edge inscription SUUM - CUIQUE.
The shape and size of the shield varies.

260   TALER 1767

SIGISMUNDUS. D:G.A.& P.S.A.S.L.N.G. PRIM., bust R.
Crowned and mantled arms with -17-67- below.

1261   TALER 1769-1771

SIGSM. D:G.A. & P.S.A.S.L.N.G. PRIM:, bust R with F.M. below.
Crowned and mantled arms with divided date below.
The shape and size of the shield varies. The 1769 has a small bust; the 1771 a large one.
Varieties of 1770: two different small busts and one large one. Date 17-70 or 1-7-7-0.
1769-1770 with edge inscription SUUM - CUIQUE; 1770-1771 decorated.

HIERONYMUS, COUNT VON COLLOREDO-WALDSEE   1772-1803

1262   TALER   1772

HIERONYMUS. D:G.A.& P.S.A.S.L.N.G. PRIM:, small bust with F.M.(F.)
Crowned and mantled oval arms with date below.
Close or wide date.

1263   TALER   1772-1786

Similar to #1262, larger bust with F.M.F. or F.M. or M. below.
Similar to #1262 with smaller mantle.
Much variety in the size of the bust and of the mantle and crown on reverse.

1264   TALER   1787-1789

Similar to #1263.
Similar to #1263, different shield and arms, close date.

265 [42]   TALER 1789-1800

Similar to #1263 with another bust.
Similar to #1264 with new shape for shield, spread date.
The 1792-1793 have close dates. The 1789 with EP./&.

266   TALER 1790

Similar to #1263 with another bust.
Crowned arms supported by two lions, date below.
Supposedly only 7 released after protests by the duke of Bavaria over the reverse design.

VIENNA

A BISHOPRIC was founded in Vienna in 1471. The bishop became a prince in 163?
and in 1722 the see was raised to an archbishopric. The territorial holdings of the
archbishopric were small and so was the coinage. The only large size silver piece
seems to be the emission of 1781.

CHRISTOF ANTON, COUNT VON MIGAZZI   (1757-1803)

1267   TALER 1781

CHRISTOPHORVS. D.M.S.R.E. CARDINALIS. DE MIGAZZI., bust R with I.W. below.
ARCHIEP. VIEN. S.R.I.P. EP. VACIEN. ADM. S. STEPH. R.A.M.C.E. 1781., carped an
crowned arms on mantle with I.C. - F.A. at sides.
2000 minted.

AUSTRIAN NETHERLANDS

(For history see Spanish Netherlands.)

M AXIMILIAN II EMANUEL, Duke of Bavaria, had been appointed governor general
of the Netherlands in 1692 by the Spanish King. Ousted from Bavaria for his pro
French policies, he was later appointed stadholder of Brabant as compensation, and i.
May 1711 Louis XIV of France put him in actual control of Namur, Luxemburg, and
Chimay. Coins were prepared from the former place in 1712-1714.

The Treaty of Utrecht gave the Belgic provinces to Austria and some years of tur
moil followed as local authorities, jealous of their liberties, resisted imperial control
However, under Maria Elizabeth, sister of Charles VI, governor general from 1725 to
1741, prosperity was restored. Charles of Lorraine, brother-in-law of Maria Theresia
governed from 1741-1780. For two years during the War of the Austrian Succession
the provinces were in French hands but were returned to the Austrians in 1748.

Joseph II provoked widespread discontent by his clerical and governmental reforms
In 1789 the Estates of Brabant rose in revolt and declared their autonomy. Other
Estates followed and an independent nation was formed in 1790. Austrian rule was
reestablished in November of that year, however, and two years later the French
Revolutionary armies invaded. By 1794 the entire region was under French control.

ARCHDUKE CHARLES OF AUSTRIA 1707-1711

268 PATAGON OF 2 PESOS 1707, 1709, 1710 (ANTWERP)
269 PATAGON 1707, 1709-1711 (ANTWERP)
CAROLUS III. D.G. HISP. ET INDIARVM REX hand (Antwerp), crown over Andreas cross, two crowned linked C's at sides.
ARCHID. AVST. DVX - BVRG. BRABANT. Z c divided date, crowned arms in order chain.
Two sizes of lettering on 1709. 1707, 1709 have U's for V's.

1270 PATAGON 1709 (BRUGES)
Similar to #1269 with lily at top.
ARCH. AUST. DUX - BURG. C. FLAND. Z c, 17 - 09, crowned arms in Order chain.

MAXIMILIAN II EMANUEL OF BAVARIA AS STADHOLDER OF BRABANT 1711-1714

1271 ECU 1712 (NAMUR)
MAX. EMANVEL - V.B.S.P.B.LL & G. DVX, lion 1712, head R with TB monogram below.
C.P.R.S.R.I.A.EL. & VIC. LL. - C.F.H.&.N.M.S.R.I.D. MECH, crowned spade shaped arms in chain.
A. Variety with unbound hair.

1272   ECU 1712 (NAMUR)
Similar to #1271.
COM. P.R.S.R.I. AR. &. ELE. L.L. - COM. F.H.&.N. MAR. S.R.I.D.M., crowned ro ir ɹ arms
in Order chain. (See #1276 for ill.)
A. Variety with no lion mintmark.

1273   ECU 1713 (NAMUR)
Same legend as #1271 with 1713, bust R.
Similar to #1271 but crowned round arms with chain close.
SR #425 has U's for V's and M for MECH.

1274   ECU 1713 (NAMUR)
Similar to #1273.
Similar to #1272. (See #1276 for ill.)

1275   ECU 1713 (NAMUR)
MAX. EMANUEL D.G. - U.B.S.P.B.L.L.&.G. DUX lion, bust R with 1713 below. (See #1276
for ill.)
Similar to #1273.

1276   ECU 1713-1714 (NAMUR)
Similar to #1275.
Similar to #1272.

1277   ECU 1714 (NAMUR)
Similar to #1275.
Similar to #1271.

Some of these types #1271-1277 are apparently mulings struck later.

CHARLES VI OF AUSTRIA 1711-1740

1278 DUCATONE OF 2 PESOS 1725

1279 DUCATONE 1721, 1725, 1729
CAROLUS VI. D.G. ROM. - IMP. HISP. ET IND. REX, bust R witn nand (Antwerp) below.
ARCH. AUST. - DUX - BURG. - BRABANT. Z c divided date, crowned and supported arms
in Order chain.
There is a gold strike of 1724.

MARIA THERESIA 1740-1780

1280 DUCATONE 1749-1754 (ANTWERP)
MAR. TH. D.G.R. - IMP. G. HUN(G). BOH. R., bust R.
ARCH. AUS. DUX. - BURG. BRAB. C. FL., crowned arms in sprays, below hand (Antwerp)
and date.
Several changes in the bust over the period, and the size of the lettering varies.

1281 DUCATONE 1750, 1754 (BRUGES)
MAR: TH: D:G:R: - IMP: G: HUN: BOH: R:, bust R.
Similar to #1280 with lion (Bruges) below arms.
The 1754 has a heavier bust and smaller lettering. A 1751 is also reported.

1282 KRONENTALER 1755-1775, 1777-1780
MAR. THERESIA D:G:R. IMP. GERM. HUNG. BOH. REG. mm., four crowns in the angles
of a floriated cross.
ARCH. AUST. DUX. BURG. BRAB. COM. FLAND. date, crowned double eagle with arms
on breast.
Hand (Antwerp) 1755-1758 ; head (Brussels) 1758-1780.

FRANCIS I   1745-1765

1283 KRONENTALER 1755-1765
FRANCIS. D. GRATIA - ROMAN. IMPERAT. S.A. mm., crowned double eagle with arms on
breast within Order chain.
GERM. JERO. REX LOTH. BAR. MAG. HET. DUX date, three crowns in angles of a
floriated cross.
Hand (Antwerp) 1755-1758 ; head (Brussels) 1758-1765.

JOSEPH II   1780-1790

1284 KRONENTALER 1781-1789
IOSEPH. II. D.G.R. IMP. S.A. GER. HIER. HUNG. BOH. REX., head R.
ARCH. AUST. DUX. BURG. LOTH. BRAB. COM. FLAN. head (Brussels) dividing date,
crowns and cross as on #1283.

INDEPENDENT PROVINCES 1790

1285 3 FLORINS 1790

DOMINI EST REGNVM., lion holding shield with LI / BER / TAS, 1790, below. DOMINABITVR GENTIVM ET IPSE, sun surrounded by 11 coats of arms.

44,534 minted.

FRANCIS II 1792-1795

1286 KRONENTALER 1794

FRANC. II. D.G.R. IMP. S.A. GER. HIER. HUNG. BOH. REX., head R. Similar to #1284.

DENMARK

DENMARK'S complete dominance of the Baltic scene passed with the extinction of the old royal line in 1448. The new kings—of the Oldenburg line—ruled Denmark and Norway, aided by the Reformation and by the struggle of burghers and peasants versus church and nobility. In spite of the emergence of an absolute monarchy about 1660, Denmark's prestige after her repulse by Sweden began to decline.

The reign of Frederick III saw the rise of a new burgher bureaucracy, which increased in power under the succeeding reign of Christian V (1670-1699). The 18th century opened for Denmark with a new king Frederick IV (1699-1730) and a renewed struggle with Sweden for the recovery of the lost territory of Skaane. The territory was not recovered but Denmark became involved in a century long controversy over the provinces of Schleswig and Holstein. Sweden was allied with the dukes of Holstein-Gottorp, and when Frederick had achieved some temporary successes, he incorporated ducal Schleswig into the Danish monarchy (1721). The Holstein-Gottorp dukes were furious but impotent, and conflict was avoided only temporarily, to blaze again when members of the family became heirs to the thrones of Sweden and Russia.

War seemed inevitable in 1761 when the Duke became Tzar of Russia as Peter III. But the disposal of Peter by his wife's orders in 1762 and the arrangement made by Catherine II to exchange ducal Gottorp for Oldenburg, which Denmark had acquired in 1673, made it possible for Denmark to take complete possession of Schleswig and Holstein in 1773.

Conditions of the peasants and tenant farmers had greatly deteriorated since 1660, but the building up of an Asian and West Indian trade in the mid-eighteenth century brought commercial prosperity and the possibility of agricultural improvement. The latter was not fully realized until the power of the land owners was broken by the king's minister Struensee in 1770. Scandal involving the minister and the queen of Christian VII nearly wrecked the movement, but Crown Prince Frederick by a coup d'etat in 1784 acquired the authority and to all intents and purposes dispossessed his father. A complete revision in landlord-peasant relations was achieved in 1788.

This period of peace and prosperity ended with the country's becoming engulfed in the Napoleonic wars, and culminated in the destruction of the Danish fleet and the bombardment of the capital by the British in 1801.

Denmark's currency during the 18th century is somewhat involved. The specie-dalers and reisedalers were the equivalent of 6 marks; the krone of 4 marks. The latter comes in double and triple denominations usually in double and triple thickness, although the 1726 triple krone is 52mm. in diameter. The speciedalers of 1747 also appeared in double thickness of double value. The reisedalers, issued to pay for the king's travel, usually in Norway, were made of Norwegian silver and were much prized by the recipients. The Albertusdalers were struck from Norwegian silver for the Baltic trade; they were deliberately made of silver finer than that of any of their competitors and were consequently circulated at a premium. The name comes from similar pieces coined in the Netherlands under Albert, archduke of Austria (1598-1621), and later copied elsewhere.

Denmark issued a piastre in 1771 and another in 1777 for trading purposes. The obverse has the king's titles and a crowned shield; the reverse a motto and the Pillars of Hercules flanking round coats-of-arms with a label below, indicating that the pieces were intended for circulation in colonial and foreign trade.

FREDERICK IV   1699-1730

287   2 KRONER 1702
FRID. IIII. D.G. DAN. NOR. VA. GO. REX., bust R.
DOMINUS. MI - HI. ADIUTOR., three crowned monograms F4 with arms between. *17 heart 02 * below. Heart for Copenhagen mint.

288   SPECIEDALER 1704
FRID. IIII. D.G. DAN. - NOR. VAN. GOT. REX., bust R.
DVX. SLES. HOLS. STORM. - DITM. COM. OLD. ET. DEL., crowned arms in double chain, *17 - 04* below.

289   REISEDALER 1704
FRID. IIII. D. - G. REX. DAN. NOR. V.C., bust R.
MOD. TROSKAB. DAPPERHED. OG HVAD DER GIVER AERE and DEN HEELE VERDEN KAND. BLANT NORSKE KLIPPER LAERE, Norwegian arms separating 6 - M with 17 heart 04 in circle.
Three varieties. A. With obverse legend FRIDERIC. IV. - D.G. REX. DAN. NOR. V.G. B. With 6 and fancy M.

H

1290   KRONE   1711, 1723

FRIDERICUS. IIII. D. - G. REX. DAN. NOR. V.G., horseman to R. In exergue IIII. MARCK / DANSKE.
DOMINUS MI - HI. ADIUTOR., crowned arms in double chain with divided date below.
The dies of the two dates are quite different with some change in the coat of arms, and there are several dies of each date.
Copenhagen (C.W.) 1711 7,905 minted. Kongsberg (H.C.M.) 1723 30,000 minted.

1291   KRONE   1724, 1726

.DOMINUS. MIHI. ADIUTOR., crowned monograms F 4.
.IIII. MARK. DANSKE. date. C (heart) W, crown in circle.
Copenhagen 1724 - 3,040 minted ; 1726 - 4,526 minted.

1292   KRONE   1725-1726

D.G. REX. DAN. - NOR. VAN. GOT° , crowned monograms F 4.
DOMINUS MIHI - ADIUTOR. date°, crowned arms in Order band with H.C-M. below.
Kongsberg 1725 - 102,555 minted ; 1726 - 139-032 minted.

293 3 KRONER 1726
FRIDER. IIII. D.G. - REX. DAN. NOR. V. GO., bust R with *DOMINUS. MIHI. ADIUTOR* below.
DUX. SLES. HOL. STOR. - DITM. COM. OLD. DELM., three arms crowned in Order chain within circle of 15 shields, 17 - 26 below.

CHRISTIAN VI 1730-1746

294 KRONE 1731-1732
CHRIST. VI. D.G. - REX. DAN. NORV. V.G., bust R.
.IIII. MARK. DANSKE. date. C (heart) W, crown and DEO ET POPVLO in circle.
Copenhagen 1731—90,164 minted; 1732—9,836 minted.

295 REISEDALER 1732-1733
Similar to #1294.
Crowned shield with Norwegian arms separating .6 - M. with date below.
Copenhagen 1732—4,534 minted; 1733—5,000 minted.
A. Variety of 1733 with fancy M in 6 - M.

1296   KRONE 1736

D.G. REX. DAN. - NORV. VA. GO., crowned monograms C 6.
IIII MARCK*C* crossed pickaxes *DANSKE*1736*, crowned Norwegian arms.
Kongsberg 4,000 minted.

FREDERICK V   1746-1766

1297   3 KRONER   N.D. (1746)

FRIDERICUS V. D.G. - REX. DAN. NOR. V.G., bust R.
CHRISTIANUS VI. D. - G. REX. DAN. NOR. V.G., bust R.
Copenhagen, triple thickness.
For the death of Christian VI and the accession of Frederick V.

1298   2 SPECIEDALERS   1747

1299   SPECIEDALER   1747

FRIDERICVS V. D. - G. REX. DAN. NOR., king on throne under canopy.
.PRVDENTIA ET CONSTANTIA., crowned and supported arms on base. 17 heart 47 in
    frame below.
For the king's coronation.

1300   2 KRONER 1747

FRIDERICUS V - DEI GRATIA., head R.
DAN. NOR. VAN. GOT. REX 17 heart 47. Crown with PRUDENTIA ET CONSTANTIA below.
Copenhagen, double thickness. A 1 krone from the same dies.

1301   REISEDALER 1749

FRIDERICUS V. D.G. REX DAN. NOR. V.G., bust R.
TROE LOVE MOD OG HVAD DAN. KONGENS GUNST KAND VINDE / MENS NORGE
   KLIPPE HAR MAND SKAL HOS NORDMAND FINDE, Norwegian arms with 17 (6M) 47
   below.
Issued by the Danish-Asiatic Co. for the 300th anniversary of the reign of the House of Olden-
   burg in Denmark.
Copenhagen, 5,008 minted. A. With initials P.C.W. B. With initial W.

1302   SPECIEDALER 1764-1765

FRIDERICUS. V. D.G. DAN. NOR. VAN. GOT. REX., head R. with D.I.A. below, 1764 only.
PRUDENTIA ET CONSTANTIA, crowned arms in sprays, date below divided by H.S.K.
Three varieties. A. With obverse like #1303 on both dates. B. Obverse legend FRIDERICUS.
   V. D.G. REX. DAN. NORV. VAND. G., head with I.H.W. on both dates.

1303   SPECIEDALER 1765

FRIDERICVS. V. D.G. DAN. NOR. V.G. REX., head R with B below.
PRUDENTIA ET CONSTANTIA., crowned Norwegian arms with 17 T crossed axes L 65. below.
Kongsberg mint.

CHRISTIAN VII   1766-1808

1304   SPECIEDALER 1767-1769

D.G. DAN. NOR. VAN. GOT. REX., crowned monograms C 7.
GLORIA. EX. AMORE. PATRIAE., crowned Norwegian arms, date below.
The crowns on both sides vary in size.
Kongsberg (T L) 1767-1768 ; Copenhagen (H S K) 1768-1769.

1305   SPECIEDALER 1769

CHRIST. VII. D.G. REX. DAN. NOR. VAN. GOT., bust R with B below.
GLORIA. EX - AMORE. PATRIAE., crowned arms in ribbon, 17.H.S.K.69. below.

1306   SPECIEDALER 1769
Similar to #1304 with different crown and thinner C's.
Similar to #1305 with larger crown.
A. Variety with *17.H.S.K.69*

1307   SPECIEDALER 1771
Similar to #1304 with smaller crown and thinner C's.
Similar to #1306 with smaller crown and sprays instead of ribbons.

1308   SPECIEDALER 1776-1781, 1785
D.G. DAN. NORV. VAND. GOTH. REX., crowned monograms C 7.
Similar to #1307 with heavier sprays.
Copenhagen (HSK) 1776, 1780; Kongsberg (HIAB) 1776-1779, 1781, 1785; Altona (CHL) 1776.

1309   SPECIEDALER 1777

D.G. REX DAN. NOR. VAN. GO. DVX SL. HOLS. ST. DIT. & OLD., crowned monograms C 7.
Similar to #1308 with 17 C.H.L. 77 and no periods in legend.
Altona mint.

1310   ALBERTUSDALER 1781, 1784, 1786, 1796

MONETA NOV. ARG. REGIS DANIAE., wildman behind crowned shield.
GLORIA EX AMORE PATRIAE, crowned arms dividing date.
Altona mint. Several dies.

1311 [70]   SPECIEDALER 1787-1791, 1794-1796, 1799-1800

CHRISTIANUS. VII. D.G. DAN. NORV. V.G. REX., head R with initials below.
60. SCHILLING. SCHLESW. HOLST. COURANT, crowned arms separating 1. - SP. with date
below.
Altona mint. Many varieties especially in heads.
Under head B on 1787-1788, 1790-1791, 1794-1796, 1799-1800; D.I. on 1787-1788; H on 1788; M
on 1788-1790; P.G. on 1799-1800.

312   REISEDALER 1788

CHRISTIAN DEN VII. DANMARKS OG NORGES KONGE, bust R.
UROKKELIG SOM DOVRES HOYE FIELDE / STAAER NORGES SONNERS TROSKAB MOD
OG VAELDE, Norwegian arms. In exergue I RIGSDALER COUR: / 17 M.F. 88.
Altona mint.

313 [71]   SPECIEDALER 1791-1792. 1795-1799

Similar to #1311.
1. RIGSDALER. SPECIES, crowned arms with divided date below.
Kongsberg (HIAB) 1791-1792 no initials under head. Altona (MF) 1795, 1797 with B under
head. Copenhagen (CHL) 1796-1797, (HIAB) 1798-1799 with B under head.

314   SPECIEDALER 1792-1795

Similar to #1311 with new coiffeur, more hair below bow.
Similar to #1313.
Kongsberg (HIAB) 1792 with S.I. under head; other dates no initials on obverse.

1315   SPECIEDALER   1799
Similar to #1313, small head with unbound hair and P.G. below.
Similar to #1313.
Copenhagen and Altona mints.

FRANCE

THE territorial possessions and prestige which France acquired under the House of Capet 987-1328 were somewhat diminished and dimmed under their successors, the cadet branch of the family, the Valois 1328-1589, at least until the close of the Hundred Years War in 1453, when some consolidation and expansion occurred. In 1589 the Bourbons inherited the throne in the person of Henry IV, king of Navarre.

The latter's assassination in 1610 was followed by the domination in France of two princes of the Church, Richelieu and Mazarin, paving the way for the grand monarch Louis XIV (1643-1715), whose reign opened with much promise, lapsed into magnificence, and ended at his death with the curses of an exhausted and disillusioned people. Among the king's efforts to finance his court and wars was a succession of currency reforms, which consisted largely of restriking older issues and raising the value of the restrikes. Thus many of the pieces of 1701-1709 are badly struck with some of the older designs showing through. The ecu carambole (#1317 and #1323) of this period with slightly larger circumference was coined to compete with the long established Lowlands ducaton in Flanders. The new issue of 1709 is somewhat heavier in weight.

Louis XV (1715-1774) was a child of five when he inherited the throne, and until he was 33 France was governed by a succession of regents and ministers culminating in Cardinal Fleury. Lorraine was acquired by the king's father-in-law in 1735 with a reversion to the French throne on his death. Louis's personal reign encompassed the Wars of the Austrian Succession 1740-1748 and the Seven Years War 1756-1763, in which France lost both prestige and overseas territory. Corsica was won in 1768. He died in 1774 no more regretted than his great grandfather before him. Louis XV's early reign was a period of chaotic financial management, and only in 1726 finally emerged an ecu with a value of 5 livres which was to survive to the Revolution, changed only in portraits.

The reign of Louis XVI (1774-1793) showed further French mismanagement in international politics and an inability to cope with home problems, despite the many good intentions of the young king. Affairs moved toward a climax and in 1789 came the Revolution and the establishment of government by the Assembly. New coins eventually marked this change to a constitutional period. Four years passed before the king was executed and republican government instituted. The completely redesigned coinage for the First Republic has for the first time the value incorporated into the design. In 1795 the monetary standard was changed to francs. This government passed through successive stages, the Directory 1795-1799, the Consulate 1799-1804, and finally into the Empire in 1804.

The coats of arms on the French ecus include the following:
France (old)—eight fleur-de-lys in a checkered border
    (new)—three fleur-de-lys
Burgundy (old)—five fleur-de-lys in a checkered border
    (new)—three diagonal stripes
Navarre—pattern of connected circles in a square
Bearn—two cows
Dauphiné—dolphin

The mintmarks appearing on the ecus during this century include the following:

A—Paris	I—Limoges	S—Reims
AA—Marsailles (Louis XIV)	K—Bordeaux	T—Nantes
Metz (Louis XV and XVI)	L—Bayonne	V—Troyes
B—Rouen	M—Toulouse	W—Lille
BB—Strasbourg	MA—Marsailles 1786-	X—Amiens
C—Caen	N—Montpelier	Y—Bourges
D—Lyons	O—Clermont (Louis XIV)	Z—Grenoble
E—Tours	Riom (Louis XV)	&—Aix
F—Angers	P—Dijon	9—Rennes
G—Poitiers	Q—Perpignan	cow—Pau
H—La Rochelle	R—Orleans	ʃ—Besançon

LOUIS XIV   1643-1715

1316   ECU 1701-1703

LVD. XIIII. D.G. - FR. ET NAV. REX., bust R.
SIT. NOMEN. DOMINI. BENEDICTVM. date, crowned arms of France with scepter and hand
of Justice behind. Mintmark below.

1317   ECU 1701-1703

Similar to #1316 with smaller head.
Similar to #1316 with four part arms of France, old and new Burgundy, and Navarre.

1318   ECU 1701-1702

Similar to #1316, with NA. RE.BD.
Similar to #1316 with three part arms of France, Navarre, and Bearn.
For Navarre-Bearn.

319   ECÚ 1702
Similar to #1316.
Similar to #1316 with arms of France and Dauphiné.
For Dauphiné.

320   ECU 1704-1709
Similar to #1316.
Legend similar to #1316 with arms of France surrounded by 4 double L's crowned with fleur-de-lys between.

321   ECU 1704
Similar to #1318.
Legend similar to #1316 with three part arms of France, Navarre, and Bearn surrounded by L's and fleur-de-lys as on #1320.

1322   ECU   1704-1705

Similar to #1316 with draped bust R.
Similar to #1320.

1323   ECU   1705

LVDOVICVS. XIIII * D.G. FR. ET. NAV. REX, bust R.
Legend similar to #1316, crowned square shield with arms of France and old and n
Burgundy.
For Flanders.

1324   ECU   1709-1715

Similar to #1316.
Legend similar to #1316 with three crowns forming triangle with fleur-de-lys between and m
initial in center.

LOUIS XV   1715-1774

$25   ECU 1715

LUD. XV. D.G. FR. ET. NAV. REX., child's bust R.
Similar to #1324.

$26   ECU 1716-1718

Similar to #1325.
Legend similar to #1316, crowned round shield with arms of France.

$27   ECU 1718-1719

LVD. XV. D.G. FR. - ET. NAV. REX., larger bust R.
Legend similar to #1316, crowned shield with four part arms of France and Navarre.
For Navarre.

1328   ECU   1720-1724

Similar to #1325 with youth's bust R.

Similar to #1327 with crowned shield with arms of France.

1329   ECU   1724-1725

Similar to #1328 with older bust R.

SIT. NOMEN. DOM. BENEDICT. date, four crowns and four double L's surround four fleu de-lys in cross form.

1330   ECU   1726-1740

Legend similar to #1325 with bust L.

Legend similar to #1325, crowned arms of France in laurel sprays.

₿31   ECU 1740-1771

LUD. XV. D. G. FR. - ET NAV. REX., head L.
Similar to #1330.

31A   ECU   1756, 1765, 1770

LUD. XV. D. G. FR. — ET NA. RE. BD., head L like #1331.
Similar to #1331 with cow mm.

332   ECU 1770-1774

Similar to #1331 with older, clothed head.
Similar to #1331.

332A   ECU   1772

Similar to #1331A with older head of #1332.
Similar to #1332.

LOUIS XVI   1774-1793

1333   ECU 1774-1792

LUD. XVI. D. G. FR. - ET NAV. REX., bust L, with B .DUVIV. F. on bust.
Similar to #1332.

1334   ECU 1778-1788

LUD. XVI. D. G. FR. - ET NA. RE. BD., bust L, with B .DUVIV.F. on bust.
Similar to #1332.
Pau mint.

1335   ECU OF 6 LIVRES 1792-1793

LOUIS XVI ROI - DES FRANCOIS., head L with date below.
REGNE DE LA LOI., angel writing on tablet with fasces at L and cock at R. Below L'AN
  (4 or 5) DE LA / LIBERTE.
Coined in the constitutional period.

REPUBLIC   1793-1795

1336   ECU OF 6 LIVRES 1793, N.D.
.REPUBLIQUE FRANCOISE. .L'AN II., in wreath in center SIX LIVRES. and mintmark.
Similar to #1335 with 1793 or nothing in exergue.

DIRECTORY 1795-1799, CONSULATE 1799-1804

1337 [81]   5 FRANCS AN 4-9 [1795-1800]
UNION ET - FORCE., Hercules, Liberty, and Equality in a group with . Dupre . below.
REPUBLIQUE FRANCAISE, 5 FRANCS and L'AN figure, in wreath with mintmark below.

GREAT BRITAIN

THE island kingdom of England after its conquest in 1066 by the Normans wa ruled by a succession of dynasties, Norman, Plantagenet, Tudor and Stuart.

The eighteenth century opened with William III (1688-1702) on the throne. He wa succeeded by his sister-in-law Anne (1702-1714). Under her in 1707 a parliamentar union with Scotland took place, and the coats of arms on Anne's coinage are appropr ately modified. The war of the Spanish Succession increased England's overseas ter tories but produced turmoil and dissention at home. In 1703 an issue of crowns appear with VIGO below the queen's bust. These were minted from silver taken from Spanis galleons when Vigo was captured by an English fleet in October 1702.

Anne was the last of the Stuart line. The succession having been fixed in the near Protestant relative of the queen, the House of Hanover in the person of its elect George Ludwig, who became George I (1714-1727), inherited the throne on Anne death. "Fidei Defensor" was added to the king's titles and the coat of arms wa changed to include the shield of Brunswick.

George II (1727-1760) succeeded his father with no basic changes in the currenc The issue of 1746 with LIMA below the bust was struck from silver captured in 174 in Spanish treasure ships loaded with South American silver by Admiral Anson in h voyage around the world. His last issue of crowns in 1751 is followed by a 68-yea gap before the denomination was again minted.

The plumes on the reverse of some of these pieces indicate that the silver came fro mines in Wales; roses were used on silver mined in the west of England; and rose and plumes mark silver supplied by the new "Company for smelting down lead wit Pitcoale and Seacoale."

ANNE　　1702-1714

1338　CROWN　1703
ANNA. DEI. - GRATIA., bust L with VIGO. below.
MAG - BR. FRA - ET. HIB - REG. 17 - 03., four crowned arms arranged in cross form.

1339　CROWN　1705
Similar to #1338 without VIGO.
Similar to #1338 with plumes in the angles of the arms.

340   CROWN 1706-1707

Similar to #1339.
Similar to #1338 with plumes and roses in the angles of the arms.

341   CROWN 1707-1708

Similar to #1339 with larger bust.
MAG - BRI: FR. - ET HIB: - REG: divided date, arms similar to #1338 but English and Scotch arms combined.
After the union of England and Scotland.

342   CROWN 1707-1708

Similar to #1341, still larger bust with E below.
Similar to #1341 with MAG:
Struck at the Edinburgh mint.

1343   CROWN 1708

Similar to #1341.
Similar to #1342 with plumes in the angles of the arms.

1344   CROWN 1713

Similar to #1341 with no . after DEI.
MAG. - BRI. FR. - ET. HIB. - REG. - 17 - 13., plumes and roses in the angles of the arms

GEORGE I   1714-1727

1345   CROWN 1716, 1718, 1720, 1726

GEORGIVS D G M. BR. FR. ET. HIB. REX F D, bust R.
BRVN - ET L. DVX - S.R.I.A:TH. - ET. EL. divided date., four crowned arms in cross form
with plumes and roses in the angles.

346   CROWN   1723

Similar to #1345.
Similar to #1345 but with SS - C - SS - C in the angles of the arms.
Struck from silver supplied by the South Sea Company.

GEORGE II   1727-1760

347   CROWN   1732, 1734-1736

GEORGIVS. II - DEI. GRATIA., bust L.
M.B.F. ET - H. REX.F.D.B. - ET. L.D.S.R.I. - A.T. ET. E. divided date, arms similar to #1345
with plumes and roses.

1348   CROWN   1739, 1741

Similar to #1347.
Similar to #1347 with only roses in the angles.

1349   CROWN 1743

GEORGIUS. II. - DEI. GRATIA., older bust L.
Similar to #1348.

1350   CROWN 1746

Similar to #1349 with GEORGIVS and LIMA. below bust.
Similar to #1348 with nothing in the angles of the arms.

1351   CROWN 1750-1751

Similar to #1349 with GEORGIVS.
Similar to #1350.

HOLSTEIN

1HE duchy of Holstein, situated at the base of the Danish peninsula north of the
▪ river Elbe and bounded by the North and Baltic seas, was long a bone of contention
:tween Danes and Germans. In 1460, altho Holstein was recognized as a fief of the
oly Roman Empire, the Danish king Christian I had been chosen count of Holstein
▪d the territory linked with the duchy of Schleswig, the king becoming duke of
:hleswig-Holstein. A series of partitions followed, one of which in 1544 established
▪ line of dukes of Gottorp with their seat in Schleswig. After years of controversy
▪enmark admitted the duke's claim of full sovereignty only in 1689. Many parts of
▪th Schleswig and Holstein were controlled jointly by the duke and the king. The
:tablished truce was allegedly broken in 1713 by the regent uncle of Karl Friedrich,
▪hristian August, and Denmark drove the young duke out of Schleswig. He was
▪stored in 1720 but ultimate Danish sovereignty was recognized the following year.
The duke married the grand duchess Anna, daughter of Peter the Great of Russia,
▪d their son Karl Peter Ulrich, duke of Holstein-Gottorp (1739-1762) was recognized
▪ the heir to the Russian throne by the Empress Elizabeth and succeeded her in 1762.
▪e was disposed of, presumably by the orders of his wife Catherine II, later in the
▪me year. In 1773 the Empress resigned all Russian rights in Schleswig and Holstein
▪ Denmark.

KARL FRIEDRICH OF HOLSTEIN-GOTTORP   1702-1739

352   TALER 1711
CAROL. FRIDER. D.G.H.N. DUX. SLES. ET HOL., bust R.
°CONSTANTIA ET LABORE. 1711 °, crowned arms separating B - H

KARL PETER ULRICH OF HOLSTEIN-GOTTORP   1739-1762

▪353   ALBERTUSTALER 1753
PETRUS. D:G. MAGNUS DUX TOTIUS RUSSIAE, bust R with S below.
HAER: NORW. DUX SLESV: HOLS: ST - & DITM: COM: OLD & DELM.1753, crowned
double eagle with arms of Russia and Schleswig Holstein.
A. Variety with bust closer to bottom rim and spelling RUSSIA.
Mannheim mint.

Friedrich Karl was the last of the dukes of Holstein-Norburg-Plön, a line found in Plön in 1622 and in Norburg in 1676. In 1729 he gave Norburg to Denmark f Plön, and after his death the latter duchy reverted to the Danish crown.

FRIEDRICH KARL OF HOLSTEIN-PLÖN   1729-1761

1354   TALER 1761

°FRIDERICVS CAROLVS D:G.H.N.D.S.H. - S. ET D C. IN O. ET D, bust R with G on ar EIN THALER NACH DEM REICHS FVS, crowned arms separating 17 - 61 with G.-A.-S. belo A. Variety on a larger flan with larger bust and arms and no initials.

1355   TALER N.D.

Similar to #1354 from another die.
Similar to #1354 without date and from another die.

SAVOY

PIEDMONT

TURIN•

MILAN•

•BELGIOJOSO
RETEONO•

VENICE

GENOA

PARMA•

MANTUA
GUASTALLA

•FERRARA

•BOLOGNA

MODENA•

LUCCA•

•FLORENCE

•PISA

LIVORNO•

TUSCANY

•ORCIANO

PAPAL
STATES

•ANCONA

•ROME

VASTO•

N
A
P
L
E
S

•NAPLES

RAGUSA•

SARDINIA

•SAN GIORGIO

•PALERMO

SICILY

ITALY
18th CENTURY

ITALY

FOR nearly a thousand years after the final collapse of the Empire of the West ir 476 the peninsula of Italy experienced conquests and invasions, consolidations and divisions, foreign rulers and native despots. Out of the welter of the late Middle Ages there emerged about 1450, at least for a brief period, a somewhat stabilized pattern a shared culture, a common language, and a growing sense of nationality. Five great cities with their various rulers dominated the scene. In addition to Milan, Venice Florence, Rome, and Naples, numerous lesser republics, communes, oligarchies, counts dukes, princes, and·ecclesiastical rulers maintained a shaky independent or semi-independent existence.

In the northwest the marquisates of Saluzzo and Montferrat were eventually to fall into the hands of the dukes of Savoy, who moved their center of interest southward from Savoy into Piedmont with their capitol at Turin. In the northeast the Republic of Venice encroached ever northward and westward. The duchies of Ferrara and Urbino came under Papal control and were amalgamated with the Papal States, as were the republic cities of Bologna and Perugia. The duchies of Milan, Mantua, Modena, Parma, and Guastalla constituted the north central states. On the western coast were the republics of Genoa, Lucca, and Florence, the latter shortly to become the Grand Duchy of Tuscany and to absorb the republic of Siena and the state of Piombino. The Papal States occupied the central peninsula, and in the south the kingdoms of Naples and Sicily were finally consolidated into a dual realm. Of the other two islands besides Sicily associated with the peninsula, Corsica belonged to Genoa and Sardinia to Aragon.

A sizable number of smaller states maintained independence of a sort, some permanently, some for limited periods of time. To the former group belong the principality of Monaco and the republic of San Marino. Other issuers of scudos and talleros belonging to the second group include Bozzolo, Casale, Correggio, Desana, Messerano, Mirandola, Piacenza, Tassarolo, as well as the four small states which coined pieces only in the 18th Century. Many others, such as Asti and Benevento, since they issued no large size silver coins, are outside our immediate interest.

BELGIOJOSO

THE lords of Belgiojoso belonged to the da Barbiano family and were related to the house of Este. They lost their ancéstral possessions in the Romagna, but became counts of Belgiojoso, a fief southeast of Pavia in Lombardy. Count Antonio I Maria was created a prince of the Empire in 1769, given the coinage right, and issued Belgiojoso's only scudo in the same year.

ANTONIO DA BARBIANO   1769-1779

1356   SCUDO 1769
ANTONIUS I. BARBIANI BELGIOJOSII ET S.R.I. PRINCEPS, bust R.
COMES CUNII LUGI MARCH, GRUMELLI. 1769, crowned, mantled, and supported arms.

BOLOGNA

A FTER several centuries, from the 12th on, of communal government, Bologna fell under various masters until it was acquired in 1506 by Pope Julius II. Under the inspiration of the French Revolution the citizens rebelled and proclaimed a popular republic, which persisted from 1796 tto 1798.

1357   SCUDO MDCCXCVI OR 1796

COMVNITAS. ET. -.SENATVS. BONON., crowned arms, date in exergue.
PRAESIDIVM - *ET * DECVS *, madonna and child above city with tree of liberty at L. In exergue .BON.DOCET.

1358   SCUDO OF 10 PAOLI 1796, 1797

POPVLVS. ET. - SENATVS. BONON., crowned arms in sprays, in exergue P. 10. date. Similar to #1357 with BON. DOCET.

1359   SCUDO OF 10 PAOLI 1796, 1797

Similar to #1358 with either BONON. or BON.
Similar to #1357 but larger madonna, new city scene, no tree, and no exergue. Many varieties in scene, punctuation, etc.

GENOA

GENOA, the principal port on the Tyrrhenian sea in northwest Italy, was the capita of a province stretching along the seacoast almost from France to Tuscany. Durin the Middle Ages in spite of perpetual internal conflict Genoa developed into a might sea power with far flung commerce and colonies. In 1339 the first doge was appointed but it was only after Andrea Doria succeeded in throwing off French and Milanes influence about 1528 that a really independent government was established and main tained up to the time of the French Revolution.

Genoa prospered after losing much trade to the East by becoming bankers and arm and fleet suppliers to the Spanish monarchy. Foreign encroachments did occur o occasions, and in 1768 France took permanent possession of Corsica, long a Genoese dependency. In 1798 Napoleon transformed the state into the short lived Liguria Republic.

1360   10 SCUDI 1712 (382 GR.)

1361   6 SCUDI 1705, 1711-1712, 1715 (230 GR.)

1362   4 SCUDI 1705-1706, 1712-1713, 1715, 1719 (152 GR.)

1363   3 SCUDI 1712-1713, 1715, 1717, 1719, 1725 (114 GR.)

1364   2 SCUDI 1702, 1704-1705, 1712-1715, 1717, 1719, (76 GR.)

1365   SCUDO LARGO 1702, 1704-1705, 1712-1715, 1719 (38 GR.)
+DVX * ET * GVBERNATORES * REIP * GENV, ornate cross with cherub heads and wings in angles.
*ET*REGE* - *EOS* - .date, initials * *, madonna and child on a cloud, two cherubs above.
Initials 1702-1706 I.B.M. 1711-1725 F.M.S.

1366   SCUDO STRETTO   1701-1702, 1704-1705, 1712-1715, 1717, 1719, 1721, 1725

+ DVX * ET * GVB * REIP * GENV, cross with stars in angles.
* ET * REGE * EOS * date, initials *, madonna and child.
Initials 1701-1705 I.B.M. 1712-1725 F.M.S.

1367   8 REALI   1715

+DVX*ET*GVBERNATORES*REIP*GENV*1715.F.M.S., crowned and supported arms over sprays.
FIRMISSIMVM*LIBERTATIS*MVNIMENTVM, clasped hands with fasces and cornucopia behind.

1368   5 LIRE   1736

+DVX*ET*GVBERNATORES*REIP*GENV*, crowned and supported arms with L 5 below.
*ET*REGE*EOS* 1736 *O*M***, madonna and child on a cloud.

1369   8 LIRE   1792-1793

DUX ET GUB. - REIP. GEN, crowned and supported arms over sprays. L. - 8. below.
NON * SURREXIT * MAJOR * date, St. John standing.

1370   8 LIRE   1793-1797

DUX. ET. GUB. - REIP. GENU., crowned and supported arms on base. L. 8 below.
NON. SURREXIT. - MAJOR. date., St. John standing.

AS THE LIGURIAN REPUBLIC   1798-1805

1371 [198]   8 LIRE   1798-1799

REPUBBLICA. - LIGURE. ANNO. I or II, shield in sprays with fasces and liberty cap
. behind. L - 8 below.
LIBERTA - EGUAGLIANZA, two standing figures. H.VASSALLO on base.

GUASTALLA

GUASTALLA is located in Emilia on the southern bank of the Po river in the modern province of Reggio. From 1403 it was ruled by the Torelli family, and sold by the ast female descendant of the line in 1539 to Ferranti Gonzaga. In 1621 it became a luchy, but in 1748 was united with Parma and Piacenza and followed their subsequent istory.

GUISEPPE MARIA GONZAGA   1729-1746

372   DUCATO OF 16 LIRE 1732

*IOS. MA. GON. GVAS. SAB. DVX. BOZ. PRIN. &., bust R with * below.
IMMORTALE DECVS* VIRTVTIS* AVITAE*, man in armor treading on devil, 1732 below.

LUCCA

LUCCA, a city and province, between Modena and Tuscany on the west coast of Italy, is of ancient origin. In the Middle Ages it suffered from a series of foreign masters ind tyrants, occasionally rising to prominence and power. By Renaissance times it lad gained independence and was governed as a democracy by a vicar of the Holy Roman Emperor. In 1628 it was transformed into an oligarchy, which was eventually iverthrown in the Napoleonic period.

373   SCUDO 1735, 1737, 1741-1744, 1747, 1749, 1750

.LUCENSIS. - RESPUBLICA., crowned heart shaped arms with LIBERTAS in sprays, date below.
SANCTUS - MARTINUS., St. Martin on horseback sharing his coat with a beggar.
There are many variations. The 1735 is smaller in size and has V's for U's and reversed N's.

K

1374   SCUDO   1750-1752, 1754

Similar to #1373 with differently shaped shield, new crown, and frame.
Similar to #1373.
Many variations. The 1752 has the shield shape of the 1753.

1375   SCUDO   1753

Similar to #1373 with differently shaped shield supported by lions on a base.
Similar to #1373.

1376   SCUDO   1754-1756

Similar to #1375 with new shape for shield and changed supporters.
Similar to #1373.

MANTUA

IN THE 12th century Mantua, a city and duchy lying in the Po valley, was under a communal form of government and subsequently joined the Lombard League. After some internal strife Ludovico Gonzaga came into power in 1328 and the Gonzaga family as counts and then dukes ruled the city until their extinction in 1708. Montferrat was acquired in 1536. In 1627 the cadet line of the French house of Nevers-Rethel inherited the duchy. It was attacked and sacked by the Austrians in 1630. In 1708 the Habsburgs claimed it as a fief of the Empire and it was ruled by them as dukes of Mantua until it fell to Napoleon in 1797.

FERDINAND GONZAGA-NEVERS 1665-1708

1377 SCUDO 1703. 1706-1707

FERD. CAR. D.G. DVX. MANT. MONT. CAR. GVAS., bust R.
CONVENIENTIA CVIQVE, war paraphernalia, date below.
Several varieties of each date. A. The 1706 with FER.D.

CHARLES VI OF AUSTRIA 1711-1740

1378 TALLERO 1736

CAROL: VI: D:G:R:I:S:A: GER: HIS: HU: BO: REX*, bust R.
ARCH: AUST: DUX: BU: ET: MANTUAE: 1736 - L. 12, crowned double eagle with Latin cross for Mantua on breast.
This is reported in a double tallero also.

MILAN

MILAN, the metropolis of Lombardy in northern Italy, was ruled by the Torriani family from 1237 to 1277 when they were defeated at the battle of Desio by the noble faction under the Visconti. This noble family, except for the years 1302 to 1310 ruled the city until they died out in 1447. After a short lived republic Francesco Sforza, who had married the Visconti heiress, conquered the city and became duke of Milan in 1450. This dynasty became extinct in 1535, and the duchy then became a dependency of Spain and was governed by the kings of Spain or their deputies until the Treaty of Utrecht in 1713. Then it was handed over to the Austrian Habsburgs, who ruled until Napoleon seized it at the end of the century.

PHILIP V OF SPAIN   1700-1713

1379   FILIPPO 1702
.PHILIPPVS. V. REX. HISPANIAR., bust R with .1702. below.
.MEDIOLANI. - .DVX. ET. C., crowned arms.
Varieties: A. with no REX; B. with ERX; C. with HISPANIA; D. with DXV for DVX.

ARCHDUKE CHARLES OF AUSTRIA   1707-1711

CHARLES VI OF AUSTRIA   1711-1740

1380   FILIPPO 1707-1708
.CAROLVS. III. REX. HISPANIAR., bust R with date below.
Similar to #1379.

1381   2 FILIPPI   1736

1382   FILIPPO   N.D., 1719-1720, 1726, 1728 1731, 1733, 1736
.CAROLVS. VI. D.G. IMP. ET. HIS. REX., bust R with date below.
Similar to #1379.
There is some doubt about the 1726 and 1731 dates.

MARIA THERESIA   1740-1780

1383   2 FILIPPI   1741, 1744

1384   FILIPPO   1741, 1743-1744, 1749
.MARIA. THERESIA. D.G. REG. HUN(G). BOH. ARCH. AUST., bust R.
Similar to #1379 with new shield and date below.

1385   SCUDO   1777
M. THERESIA. D.G. - R. IMP. HU. BO. REG., bust R.
MEDIOLANI. - DUX. 1777, crowned arms over sprays.
This is probably a pattern.

1386   SCUDO   1778-1780

M. THERESIA. D.G.R. IMP. HU. BO. REG. A.A., veiled bust R.
MEDIOLANI - DUX. date, crowned arms over sprays.

JOSEPH II   1780-1790

1387   SCUDO   1781-1786

IOSEPH. II. D.G.R. IMP. S. AUG. G.H. ET B. REX A.A., head R.
MEDIOLANI ET - MANT. DUX date, crowned arms in sprays, with L B below.

1388   CROCIONE   1786-1790

IOSEPH. II. D.G.R.I.S.A. GER. HIE. HVN. BOH. REX., head R, M below.
ARCH. AVST. DVX. BVRG. LOTH. BRAB. COM. FLAN. date., St. Andrew's cross with three
crowns in angles.

LEOPOLD II   1790-1792

1389   CROCIONE   1791-1792

LEOPOLD. II. D.G.R.I.S.A. GER. HIE. HVN. BOH. REX, head R, M below.
Similar to #1388.

FRANCIS II   1792-1797, 1799-1800

1390   CROCIONE   1792-1796, 1799-1800

FRANCISC. II. D.G.R.I.S.A. GER. HIE. HVN. BOH. REX., head R, M below.
Similar to #1388.

MODENA

MODENA, in Emilia on the southern side of the Po valley, came under the rule of Obizzo d'Este in 1288. The d'Este family with several interruptions reigned until 1859. Modena was made a duchy in 1452 and after Ferrara became incorporated into the Estates of the Church in 1598, it became the residence of the ducal family. Francis III was responsible for many civic improvements. Hercules III was driven from his duchy by the French in 1796 and died in exile. Modena was transformed into the Cispadine Republic.

RINALDO D'ESTE   1706-1737

1391   DUCAT 1719-1721

RAYNALDVS. I. MVT. REG. E(C or R). D. XI. MI. I. (:), bust R, date below.
. PROTECTOR. NOSTE(R). : ASPICE. : , St. Gontard kneeling with 160 at L.
Many punctuation variations.

FRANCESCO III D'ESTE   1737-1780

1392   SCUDO 1739

FRANCISCVS. III. MUT. REG. MIR. DUX., bust R with 1739 below.
VETERIS MONU - MENTUM DECORIS, crowned arms.
A. Variety with rev. division MONVME - NTVM.

ERCOLE III D'ESTE   1780-1796

1393   TALLERO OF 3 SCUDI   1782-1783

HERCVLES. III. D.G. MVT. REG. MIR. EC. DVX., bust L with FSL on arm.
PROXIMA - SOLI, crowned shield.
The 1782 has the date after SOLI. The 1783 has it under the arms.

1394   TALLERO   1795-1796

Similar to #1393 with older bust and P.T. on arm.
DEXTERA. DOMINI* - *EXALTAVIT. ME. date, crowned arms with flags behind.
A. Varieties of both dates without the EC.

NAPLES AND SICILY

NAPLES and Sicily as a kingdom originated in 1130 and had maintained an inter-mittent unity under a succession of dynasties when Alphonzo of Aragon was recognized as king in 1443. On his death in 1458 Naples went to his illegitimate son Ferdinand, and Sicily, Sardinia, and Aragon to his brother John. By 1502 all of the Italian territories were in Spanish hands, and in 1522 Naples became an integral unit in the Spanish kingdom.

Periods of disorder followed until 1707 when the Austrians conquered Naples and brought an end to Spanish rule on the Italian mainland. At the Peace of Utrecht, 1713, Sicily was handed over to Savoy and Victor Amadeo became king. He was forced to return it to Spain in 1718, but in 1720 Sicily was given to Austria and Sardinia turned over to Victor Amadeo. The Treaty of the Escorial in 1733 between France, Spain, and Savoy against Austria was signed, and Don Carlos, son of Philip V of Spain, con-quered the twin kingdoms. In 1735 he was recognized as king with Spain renouncing all rights. After a twenty year reign marked by many needed reforms, he inherited the Spanish throne in 1759, abdicated his Naples one in favor of his eight year old son Ferdinand, who became Ferdinand IV of Naples and III of Sicily. A regency of eight years followed before Ferdinand became of age in 1767. The following year he married Maria Carolina, a daughter of Maria Theresia of Austria.

After the French Revolution Naples joined the coalition against France in 1793 and declared war in 1798. Upon Napoleon's return from Egypt the French marched on Naples and took the city on January 20, 1799. The court fled to Palermo, the capital of Sicily, and the Parthenopean Republic was set up in Naples. After only a few months this fell before Cardinal Ruffo aided by Lord Nelson's fleet. Upon his return to Naples, Ferdinand instituted a reign of terror in which many leading citizens of the state perished.

Two separate coinages, one for Naples with a shield reverse and another for Sicily with eagle reverse, were issued concurrently. The former are in denominations of piastres, ducats, and grani; the latter in piastres and taris.

NAPLES

CHARLES VI OF AUSTRIA   1707-1734

1395   DUCAT 1715

CAR. VI. DG. - .ROM. IMPE., bust R with JM on arm.
.HISP. VTRI. - .SICI. REX., - crowned arms with 17 - 15 below and MF/A in upper L.

1396 PIASTRA 1731, 1733
CAROL: VI: - D:G: ROM: IMP:, bust R with D.G; below and V.M. and .A.ᵉat L.
UTR. SIC: - HIERUS:, crowned arms with date and L. 120 below.

CHARLES OF BOURBON 1735-1759

1397 PIASTRA 1734-1736, 1747
CAR: D:G: REX NEA(P): - HISP: INFANS. &(c)., crowned arms separating F: - B:/.A. with G:120 below.
DE SOCIO PRINCEPS, river god with volcano, below DE date .G: or G. date .H.
Many varieties. A 1735 with unbroken obverse legend. Three different edge patterns. The 1747 has M - M/A.

1398 PIASTRA 1747
.CAR. UTR. SIC. REX. - & MAR. AMAL. REG., accolated busts R.
FIRMATA SECURITAS, seated woman with child, monograms at side, R. at R and DAG at L. In exergue CAR. & AMAL: PHILIPP. / POPUL SPES. NAT. / A. 1747.
On the birth of Prince Philip.

1399   PIASTRA   1748-1749

Similar to #1397 with monograms MV and MM at sides of arms and R.
Similar to #1397 with D: date .G: below.

1400   PIASTRA   1750, 1752-1754

CAR. D.G. UTR. - SIC. ET HIER. REX., bust R with DeG. below.
HISPANIAR. - INFANS. date., crowned arms with monograms and R. at sides and R. with G.
120 below.
A. There is a lighter weight 1750 with DeG. on the bust.

FERDINAND IV   1759-1799

1401   PIASTRA   1766

FERDINAND(VS). IV. D.G. - SICILIAR. ET HIER. REX., bust R with F.A. below.
HISPANIAR. - INFANS 1766, crowned arms in frame separating C. - C. and R. with GR.
120 in frame below.

402 PIASTRA 1767

Similar to #1401 with smaller bust and unbroken legend.
Similar to #1401.

403 PIASTRA 1772

FERDINANDVS REX MARIA CAROLINA REGINA, accolated busts separating C. - C. Below NEAP. MDCCLXXII.

FECUNDITAS, seated mother with child, below M. THERESIA. NATA / NON. IVNI. B.P. at left, R. at right.

On the birth of Princess Maria Theresia.

404 DUCAT OF 100 GRANI 1784-1785

FERDINAN. IV. D.G. SICILIAR. ET. HIE. REX, bust R, name or initials below.

HISPANIAR(VM). - INFANS(.) date, crowned arms separating C(.) - C(.) with DUCATO NAP. / G(RA). 100 below.

The two dates differ in many details. The 1784 has GRA. 100 and the 1785 G. 100. The 1784 below the bust has P. or PERG. or PERGER. The 1785 has B.P. or PERGER.

1405   PIASTRA   1784-1785

Similar to #1404 with different punctuation and larger bust.
HISPANIAR. - INFANS date, crowned arms separating C. - C. with small C. in upper le
and G 120 in frame below.
P. or B.P. under the bust.

1406   PIASTRA   1786-1794

Similar to #1405.
Similar to #1405 with sprays draped over shield and large G. 120 in sprays below.
Initials B.P. on 1786, 1788; D.P. on 1787; P on 1788-1794.
A variety of the 1793 and 1794 with reverse similar to #1409.

1407   PIASTRA   1791

FERDINANDVS IV. ET MARIA CAROLINA, accolated busts. R.
PRO FAVSIO PP. REDITV V.S., two figures with volcano in background, A.P. / M. at rig
and 1791 below.

408   PIASTRA   1791

FERDINANDVS IV. ET M. CAROLINA VNDIQ. FELICES, accolated busts R with P. below.
SOLI REDVCI, zodiac band, sun, earth, A.P. / M. at left and 17 - 91 below.

409 [161]   PIASTRA   1795-1800

Similar to #1405 with head R and P. below.
Similar to #1406 with initials A. - P. at sides and M. above.

AS THE PARTHENOPEAN REPUBLIC   1799

410   PIASTRA ANNO 7 (1799)

REPUBBLICA - NAPOLITANA, standing figure.
ANNO SETTIMO DELLA LIBERTA, and in a wreath CAR / LINI / DODI / CI
A. Variety with NAPOLITAN

SICILY

CHARLES III OF AUSTRIA   1720-1734

1411   SCUDO   1730-1731

CAROLVS III* DEI* GRATIA*, bust R with *C*P. below.
REX - SICILIAE* - ET. HIER., crowned eagle separating S - M with .date. below.
Some punctuation differences in the two dates.

1412   SCUDO   1732

.CAROL. - .III. D. G., head R with C.P. below.
REX. - SIC. ET - .HIE, crowned eagle separating S - M with .1732. below.

1413   ONZA OF 30 TARI   1732   (57 MM.)

CAROL. III. D.G. SICIL. ET. HIER. REX., head R with C.P. below.
.OBLITA. EX. AVRO. ARGENTEA. RESVRGIT. 1732, sun over phoenix rising from flames
S - M below.

1414   ONZA OF 30 TARI   1733   (55 MM.)

Similar to #1413.
.EX. AVRO ARGENTEA RESVRGIT. 1733, phoenix similar to #1413.

CHARLES OF BOURBON   1735-1759

415   SCUDO 1735
CAROLVS. D.G. SIC. - ET. HIER. REX. HISP. INF, bust R.
FAVSTO - CORONATIONIS - ANNO. 1735., crowned eagle separating F - N.
On his coronation.

FERDINAND III   1759-1825

416   ONZA OF 30 TARI 1785 (55 MM.)
FERDINANDVS. D. G. SICIL. ET. HIER. REX., bust R with 1785. below.
EX. AVRO. ARGENTEA. RESVRGIT., sun over phoenix rising from flames separating G.L. - C.

417   PIASTRA 1785
FERDINANDVS. D.G. SICIL. ET. HIER. REX., bust R with 1785. below.
HISPAN. - INFANS., crowned eagle separating G.L. - C.

418   PIASTRA 1786
Similar to #1417 with 1786 at end of legend and larger head.
Similar to #1417 with unbroken legend and smaller eagle.

1419   PIASTRA   1787-1790

Similar to #1417 without date.
HISPA - NIARVM. IN - FANS, crowned eagle separating G.L. - C. with date below.

1420   ONZA OF 30 TARI 1791 (57 MM.)

FERDINANDVS. D. G. SICIL. ET. HIER. REX, large bust R.
EX AVRO ARGENTEA RESVRGIT. 1791., sun over phoenix in flames separating G.L. - C

1421   PIASTRA   1793

Similar to #1419 with changed bust.
HISPA - NIA - RVM. - INFANS., crowned eagle separating N.d - O.V. with 1793(.) belo
Large and small lettering.

1422   ONZA OF 30 TARI 1793 (47 MM.)

FERDINAN. D.G. - SICIL. ET. HIER. REX., bust R with T. 30 below.
EX. AVRO. - ARGENTEA - RE - SVRGIT. 1793., sun over phoenix in flames separatin
N.d. - O.V.

423 PIASTRA 1794-1795

Similar to #1421 with **T** 12 under bust.
Similar to #1421.
One variety of the 1795 has a small break in the legend over the head.

424 PIASTRA 1796-1799

Similar to #1423 with break in the legend over the head and T. 12. below.
Similar to #1423 with arms on the eagle's breast.
There are many varieties. FERDINAN. on 1797-1799. U's for V's on reverse. The obverse legend broken in various places. A 1799 variety with unbroken legend.

425 [163] PIASTRA 1799-1800

FERDINAN. III. D.G. (-) SICIL. ET. HIER. REX., bust R with T. 12. below.
Similar to #1424 with initials J.V. - I.
Both dates with broken or unbroken obverse legend.

ORCIANO

ORCIANO, in the commune of Santa Lucia in the province of Pisa, was granted to the Obizzi family with the title of marquis in 1630 as a fief of the grand duke Ferdinand II of Tuscany. Apparently the sovereign rights had been rescinded by 1778 so at the time of the striking of the pieces in the 1790's only the title remained. Thus the pieces are probably only medals.

TOMMASO OBIZZO   1791-1796

1426   SCUDO 1791

THOMAS. ORCIANI. ET S.R.I. MARCHIO. VN. CR. BO. COM. &, bust R with LS below.
PROXIMA. FISICA. FINIS. MDCCXCI., crowned and mantled arms.
This is possibly only a medal.

1427   SCUDO 1796

Similar to #1426 with LS under bust.
BARBARAE QVIRINI / SPONSAE DVLCISSIMAE / MORIBVS INGENIO / PRAECLARAE / INTEMPESTIVA MORTE / PEREMPTE DIE XXIII OCT / THOMAS OBICIVS / MOERENS / MEMORIAM PERENNAT / A.S. MDCCXCVI.
On the death of his betrothed. Possibly only a medal.

PAPACY

AS THE Roman Empire declined the Christian Church at Rome gained in temporal power, until by the ninth century land in many parts of the Roman world and a concentration of possessions in central Italy were held by the pontiff in Rome. Members of the clergy directed the civil and military officials in administering the estates. The Popes were elected by the principal members of the clergy and nobles and actually at first, later theoretically, acclaimed by the people. During the Middle Ages, and even after the Reformation, the Popes exercised a tremendous influence on the entire civilized world.

In the fifteenth century after the period of the Babylonian captivity of the Church, when the Popes resided at Avignon, and after the great schism, when for a time there were three Popes, the last vestiges of the independence of the Roman citizens vanished, and the Popes took up permanent residence in the Eternal City as the center of their temporal domains. These came gradually to encompass all the center section of the Italian peninsula from the Tyrrhenian sea to the Adriatic and included such cities as Bologna, Ferrara, Ancona, Perugia, Ravenna, Urbino, Rimini, and Viterbo, several of which had mints in which Papal coins were minted from time to time.

From the Peace of Westphalia (1648) on, the history of the Papacy is one of gradual decline in prestige and influence, and steady increase in financial troubles. The Treaty of Utrecht (1713) ignored the Papal wishes, and during the following decades Sicily, Sardinia, and other Italian states were handed back and forth between Habsburgs and Bourbons with no Papal sanction. Parma and Piacenza were removed from any Papal authority. In 1773 such was the pressure on the Pope that the Society of Jesus, the famous order of Jesuits, was abolished. On the brighter side was the curbing of nepotism, the curse of the previous two centuries of Papal history.

Pius VI, vainly struggling against decentralization and financial chaos, saw the Church collapse in France in 1789 and then faced a decade of attempting to stem the tide of revolution. In 1797 he gave up the northern half of the Papal States, Avignon, and Venaissin, but the French army continued to advance on Rome, took the city, and carried His Holiness off to exile in France, where he died in 1799. The establishment of the Roman Republic in the city followed. (See Roman Republic)

CLEMENT XI 1700-1721

428   SCUDO   1700

CLEMENS. XI - PONT. MAX. AN. I., bust R with S.V.R. below.
PORTAM. SANCTAM. CLAVSIT. A. IVBILEI. MDCC., the Holy Door with shield and RO -
MA below.
A. Variety with no initials under bust.
Rome mint.

1429 **SCUDO 1702**
CLEMENS. XI. PONT - MAX. A. II, bust L with BORNER below.
DILEXI. DE - COREM. DOMVS. TVAE, Madonna and child, saints and Pope Innocent II. O
pedestal P.P.B. and 1702. in exergue.
For the restoration of the basilica of the Church of St. Mary in Trastevere.
Rome mint.

1430 **SCUDO 1702**
Similar to #1429 with BORNER.F below bust.
DOMINVS ELEGIT TE HODIE, St. Clement seated on a cloud with 1702 at lower L an
P.P.B. at R.
For the elevation of the pontiff.
Rome mint.

1431 **SCUDO 1703**
CLEMENS. XI. - PONT. M. A. III, arms of the Pope with P - P below.
IN. HONOREM. S. THEODORI. MAR., church of St. Theodore al Palatino with .1703. below
Rome mint.

432   SCUDO 1704
Similar to #1431, shape of shield changed, AN. IV and no initials.
VIDERVNT. OCVLI. MEI. SALVTARE. TVVM., the presentation of Jesus in the Temple.
.1704. below.
For the purification.
Rome mint.

433   SCUDO ANNO VI
CLEMENS. XI. PONT - MAX. A. VI, bust L with BORNER.F below.
The Pope on his throne surrounded by his court. BASILIC   LIBER at R. On step of throne
F. SEUO. In exergue VOX DE shield THRONO.
Rome mint.

434   SCUDO ANNO VI
Similar to #1431 with A. VI
Similar to #1433.
Rome mint.

1435   SCUDO ANNO VI
.CLEMENS. XI. - .P. M. ANN. VI., arms of the Pope with festoons at the sides. .E - H. below
Similar to #1433.
Rome mint.

1436   SCUDO ANNO VI
CLEMENS * XI * - P * M * AN * VI, bust L with HERMAN: HAMERANVS below.
St. Peter in a boat, shield below.
Rome mint.

1437   SCUDO 1707
Similar to #1436 with AN. VII and HERMANIG. HAMERANVS.
DONA * NOBIS * PACEM *, St. Clement kneeling with Peace behind. In exergue MDC - CVII
and shield.
Rome mint.

438 SCUDO ANNO VII
CLEMENS. XI - P. M. ANN. VII, arms of the Pope in festoons.
FIAT PAX / IN VIRTVTE / TVA in ornate frame with shield below.
Rome mint.

439 SCUDO 1708
CLEMENS. XI - P. M. AN. VIII, bust L with B. COTEL below.
S. GEORGIVS - FERRARIAE PROTEC, St. George on horseback slaying dragon. 17 shield 08 below.
Ferrara mint.

440 SCUDO 1709
CLEMENS * - * XI * P * M * A * IX, arms of the Pope with FER - RARIA and 17 - 09 below.
IN / TESTIMONIA / TVA * ET NON IN / AVARITIAM in frame over shield in a cartouche.
Ferrara mint.

1441   SCUDO ANNO IX
Similar to #1435 with ANN * IX * and no festoons.
Similar to #1438.
Rome mint.

1442   SCUDO 1710
CLEMENS * XI * * * PONT * M * A * X *, bust L with CIV. FER shield RARIAE.
NON / AVRVM. / SED / NOMEN./ 17 - 10 in frame over arms in cartouche.
Ferrara mint.

1443   SCUDO ANNO XI
CLEMENS * XI * - * P * M * ANN * XI, arms of the Pope.
.PROSPERVM. ITER. FACIET., view of the city and the Civita Castellana bridge. Below .PONS
    - CIVIT: / CASTEL / LANE (or LANAE) / .E. - .H. and shield.
Rome mint.

444   SCUDO OF 80 BOLOGNINI 1712-1713
CLEMENS * XI * - * PONT * MAX *, arms of the Pope with .C - F. below.
* BONONIA * DOCET, .17 - 12 separated by arms of a foliated cross. Two shields below
with * 80 * between.
Bologna mint.

445   SCUDO ANNO XIII
* CLEMENS * XI - P * M * AN * XIII *, arms of the Pope.
FONTIS ET / FORI ORNAMEN:, Piazza of the Pantheon with fountain and obelisque. In
exergue .E.H. and arms.
Rome mint.

1446   SCUDO ANNO XIII
Similar to #1445.
.FONTIS. ET. FORI - ORNAMENTO.*., obelisque and fountain of the Piazza of the Pantheon,
shield below.
Rome mint.

1447   SCUDO ANNO XV
CLEMENS * XI * - * P * M * AN * XV, bust L with HAMERANVS.F. below.
Arms of the Pope.
Rome mint.

1448   SCUDO ANNO XV
CLEMENS * - * XI * P * M * A * XV, bust R with .E.H. below.
Arms of the Pope.
Rome mint.

1449   SCUDO 1717
CLEMENS * XI * - * P * MAX * AN * XVII *, bust R with A.B. below.
DEFLVIT, / ET / INFLVIT / * 1717 * in ornate frame. ERID and reclining river god below.
Ferrara mint.

INNOCENT XIII   1721-1724

450   SCUDO OF 80 BOLOGNINI 1721
.INNOCENTIVS. - XIII. PON. MAX., arms of the Pope with 80 below.
* BONONIA * DOCET *, 17 - 21 separated by arms of foliated cross. Two shields below with
*A*B* between.
Bologna mint.

451   SCUDO OF 80 BOLOGNINI 1721
- INNOCENTIVS * - * XIII. PON * M *-*, arms of the Pope with A - B below.
Similar to #1450 with differently shaped shields and 80 between.
Bologna mint.

1452   SCUDO OF 80 BOLOGNINI 1722-1724
* INNOCENT * XIII * - * PONTE * MAX ***, arms of the Pope with A - B below.
Similar to #1451.
Bologna mint.

SEDE VACANTE 1724

1453   SCUDO 1724
* SEDE * - * VACANTE *, arms of Cardinal Albani.
.NESCIT. TARDA. MOLIMINA., dove in radiant light and clouds, shield below separating
MDCC - XXIV.
Rome mint.

1454   SCUDO OF 80 BOLOGNINI 1724
* SEDE. VACANTE. 1724 *, two shields surmounted by keys and pavilion with A * B below.
.BONONIA * DOCET., foliated cross with 80 below.
Bologna mint.

CLEMENT XII   1730-1740

1455   SCUDO 1731
CLEMENS - XII. PONT. MAX., bust R with HAMERANI below.
FOEDVS. EST. - INTER. ME. ET. TE, under a wreath seated figures of Abundance and
Justice. Below shield separating MDCC - XXXI.
Rome mint.

SEDE VACANTE 1740

456   SCUDO 1740
SEDE. VACAN - TE. MDCCXL., arms of Cardinal Albani.
EMITTE. COELITVS. LVCIS. TVAE. RADIVM, dove in radiant light and clouds.
Rome mint.

BENEDICT XIV   1740-1758

1457   SCUDO OF 9 GIULII 1740
BENEDICTVS: XIV. - P. M. BONONIENSIS, arms of the Pope.
BONONIA - DOCET, foliated cross with two shields below and .1740. between.
Bologna mint.

1458   SCUDO OF 9 GIULII 1741
BENEDICTVS. XIV. P. M. ET. ARCH. BON., bust L.
Decoration PASTORI / ET / PRINCIPI. / SENATUS / BONONIENSIS / MD
    decoration.
Bologna mint. Probably only a medal.

1459   SCUDO   1753-1754

BENED. XIV. - PONT. MAX. AN. XIV or XV, bust R with O. HAMERANI below.
MDCC - LIII or MDCC - LIV, figure representing Church seated on clouds, small shield at lower R.
Rome mint.

1460   SCUDO OF 9 GIULII ANNO XVII

BENEDICT. XIV . P . M . BONON. A. XVII, bust R.
VNVM / OMNIVM VOTVM / SALVS / PRINCIPIS / S.P.Q.B.
Bologna mint. Probably only a medal.

1461   SCUDO OF 9 GIULII ANNO XVII

Similar to #1460.
PATRIA / ET / SCIENTIARVM / INSTITVTO / MAGNIFICE / AVCTO / S.P.Q.B.
Bologna mint. Probably only a medal.

SEDE VACANTE   1758

462   SCUDO 1758
SEDE. VACAN - TE. MDCCLVIII, arms of Cardinal Colonna.
VBI. UVLT. SPIRAT., dove in radiant light and clouds. Below shield separating SCV - DO.
Rome mint.

CLEMENT XIII   1758-1769

463   SCUDO 1759
CLEMENS. XIII. - PONT. MAX. AN. I., arms of the Pope.
SVPRA. FIRMAM PE - TRAM, figure of the Church seated on clouds. shield below and 1759
at lower R.
Rome mint.

SEDE VACANTE   1774-1775

464   SCUDO OF 80 BOLOGNINI 1774
SEDE. VACAN - TE. MDCCLXXIV, two shields under keys and pavilion.
S * PETRONIO * PRO - TECTOR * BONON, kneeling saint with tower in background and
* 80 * below.
Bologna mint.

M

1465   SCUDO OF 80 BOLOGNINI 1775

* SED * VA - C * - M - DCCLXXV., two shields under keys and pavilion.
S . PETRON * PR - OT . BON ., kneeling saint with city in the background and * 80 * below
Bologna mint.

PIUS VI   1775-1799

1466   SCUDO OF 80 BOLOGNINI 1775

* PIVS * VI * PON * - * MAX * A * I *, arms of the Pope, 17 - 75 below.
Similar to #1465.
Bologna mint.

1467   SCUDO OF 80 BOLOGNINI 1775

* PIVS. VI . PON. MAX. - .ANNO. IVBILAEI., arms of the Pope, 17 - 75 below.
S. PETRONIVS - BON. PROT., seated saint with F B and 80 below.
Bologna mint.

468   SCUDO OF 80 BOLOGNINI ANNO I

PIVS. VI. PON. - MAX. AN. I., arms of the Pope.
S. PETRONIVS - BON. PROT., kneeling saint with view of the city in background and 80.
below.
Bologna mint.

469   SCUDO OF 100 BOLOGNINI 1777-1778

* PIVS. VI. PON. - MAX. AN. III or IIII *, arms of the Pope with divided date below.
S. PETRONIVS - BON. PROT, saint standing flanked by two shields and * 100 * below.
Two different shields at L on the 1777.
Bologna mint.

470   SCUDO OF 100 BOLOGNINI 1780

Similar to #1469 with AN. VI and 17 - 80.
Similar to #1469 with differently shaped shields.
Bologna mint.

1471   SCUDO 1780

PIVS SEXTVS - PONT. M. A. VI., arms of the Pope.
AVXILIVM - DE - SANCTO, figure of the Church seated on clouds, shield below and 1780 a
lower R.
Several varieties. One with AUXILIUM.
Rome mint.

1472   SCUDO 1780

Similar to #1471, new frame for arms.
Similar to #1471 with an A in the field at center L.
Ancona mint. Probably struck in 1799.

1473   SCUDO OF 100 BOLOGNINI 1782

* PIVS * SEXTUS * PONT * MAX * AN * VIII, bust R with P.T. below.
ADVENTVS. OPT - IMI. PRINCIPIS., rotunda flanked by two shields, below BONONIA. 1782
/ .100.
There are three varieties. A. With legend PIVS VI. B. Another bust with changed stole and
initials V.C. below.
Bologna mint.

1474   SCUDO 1782

Similar to #1473.
Similar to #1473 but in exergue .BONONIA. / * 1782 *
Bologna mint.

1475   SCUDO OF 100 BOLOGNINI 1795

PIVS. VI. - PONT. MAX., arms of the Pope flanked by two shields and 1795 in exergue.
S * PETRONIVS - BONON * PROT *, saint seated on a cloud, view of the city below, and in
exergue 100.
A. Variety without the value.
Bologna mint.

PARMA

THE duchy of Parma, in Emilia in the Po valley, after passing thru the hands of Correggio, Visconti, and Sforza families, in 1512 became subject to the Papacy. In 1545 Pope Pius III (Alexander Farnese) gave Parma and Piacenza to his son Pierluigi. After eight dukes of this line the duchy passed to Prince Carlos of Spain. For seventeen years it was bandied back and forth between Spain and Austria until in 1748 as a part of the settlement of the War of the Austrian Succession Maria Theresia made it over to Prince Philip of Spain. This Bourbon line continued from father to son until French revolutionary forces overran the duchy in 1796. Ferdinand bought his security and continued nominally as ruler until his death in 1802.

PHILIP OF BOURBON   1748-1765

1478   FILIPPO 1751

PHILIPPUS D.G. - HISPAN INFANS, head L.
PARMAE PLAC. ET VASTAL. DUX 1751, crowned arms.

FERDINAND OF BOURBON   1765-1802

1479   DUCATO 1784

FERDINANDVS. I. HISP. INFANS. ⁕ ., head R.
D.G. PARMAE. PLAC. - VAST. DVX. 1784, crowned arms in chain.

480   DUCATO 1786, 1789-1790

Similar to #1479 with HISPAN. and ° under head and SILIPRA on neck.
D.G. PARMAE PLAC. ET VAST. DVX date, crowned arms in leafy frame with S below.

481   DUCATO   1796-1797, 1799

Similar to #1480.
Similar to #1480 with much smaller crown.

RETEGNO

RETEGNO, a town near Codogno southeast of Milan, was given in 1654 by the Emperor Ferdinand III to Cardinal G. G. Teodoro, a member of the Trivulzio family, which held the county of Misox in Switzerland. He was made free baron of Retegno, with the mint right. The line died out in 1678, but in 1679 a cousin on his mother's side of the last baron was confirmed in possession of the barony by Leopold I, as well as in Misox. His son Antonio Tolomeo (1707-1767) was confirmed in his rights to Retegno, Misox, and Mesocinatal by Charles VI in 1712. He died in 1767 without heirs leaving his property to a philanthropic foundation.

ANTONIO TOLOMEO GALLIO-TRIVULZIO   1707-1767

1482   TALLERO 1726

ANT: PTOLOM: - TRIVULTIUS., bust R.
S.R.I. PRINC. & BARO. RETENY. IMP. 1726, crowned and mantled arms.
There is a variety with the V missing in TRIVULTIUS.

ROMAN REPUBLIC

GENERAL BERTHIER occupied Rome with a French army in February 1798 and on the 15th the Roman people declared a republic and abolished the temporal power of the Pope. Pius VI refused to abdicate but was removed from the city to France where he died. In November 1799 the Austrian General Mack took possession of the Papal States in the name of Ferdinand IV of the Two Sicilies. Following military occupation the city issued coins in Ferdinand's name. The new Pope, Pius VII, returned to the city in July 1800.

1483   SCUDO AN 6

Eagle in wreath on podium with fasces. Banner with REP. ROMANA.
ALLE / SPERANZE / DELLA. GIOUENTV / LA. PATRIA / A. 6(.)

484 **SCUDO AN VII**

Similar to #1483 completely redesigned and banner with REPUBLIC / ROMANA. / and T.M on the base.
GIORNO CHE VALE DI TANTI ANNI IL PIANTO; in center cap LIBERTA / ROMANA / XXVII / PIOVOSO / AN. VII with TM at bottom.

485 **SCUDO N.D.**

Similar to #1483
Outer legend similar to #1484; in center LIBERTA / ROMANA / 27 / PIOVOSO.

486 **SCUDO N.D.**

REPVBLICA - ROMANA, Liberty with fasces and cap on pole. Below base with or without T MERCANDETTI.
SCVDO / ROMANO in wreath.

1487   SCUDO AN VII

REPUBLICA - ROMANA*, eagle, below PERUGIA / A. VII
SCUDO in wreath
Struck at the Perugia mint.

ISSUED UNDER THE NEAPOLITAN OCCUPATION OF ROME   1799-1800

1488   SCUDO 1800

Three lilies, FERDINANDUS / IV / UTR. SIC. / REX, all in wreath.
AUXILIUM - DE - SANCTO - 1800,figure seated on a cloud. Below G. HAMERANI.

1489   SCUDO 1800

Three lilies, FERDINANDUS / IV / NEAP. ET. SIC. REX / MDCCC, all in wreath.
RELIGIONE - DEFENSA, Religion standing, G. HAMER. on base, ROMA in exergue.

SAN GIORGIO

AN GIORGIO, 33 kilometers from Palmi in the province of Reggio, had been a feudal fief of the Spanish kings. In 1731 Giovanni Domenico, marchese of San Giorgio and Polistina, was made a ince of the Empire by Charles VI with permission to strike coins. He and his son each struck udos for a single year at the Vienna mint.

GIOVANNI DOMENICO MILANO

490   SCUDO   1732

IOAN: DOMINIC: - MILANO. D.G.S.R.I.P., bust R.

MARCH: SANC:GEORGII & POLISTINAE, 1732 crowned and mantled arms.

GIACOMO FRANCESCO MILANO

491   SCUDO   1753

JAC. FR. MILANO - MARCH. SANC. GEORGII, bust R with I.C.ROETTIERS.F. below.

ET: POLESTINAE: PRINC. ARDORIS. ET. SAC. ROMANI. IMP. &.&. 1753, crowned and mantled arms.

SAVOY-SARDINIA

THE House of Savoy, the ex-royal family of Italy, descends from Humbert the White Handed, who was count of Salmourenc in 1003. He obtained the Val d'Aosta and then the county of Savoy from Conrad, king of Burgundy. His descendants became counts of Savoy in 1125, dukes of Aosta in 1238, princes of the Empire in 1310, and dukes of Savoy in 1416. In 1450 they added the rather meaningless titles of king o Cyprus, Jerusalem, and Armenia, in the family of the duke's wife, a member of the Lusignan dynasty.

Two centuries of alliances intermittently with France, then Austria, then Spain sometimes ravage the country as a battleground and added little to the boundaries or to the strength of the duchy. Victo Amedeo II (1675-1730) became involved in the War of the Spanish Succession, and by the Treaty e Utrecht in 1713 he received the duchy of Montferrat and Sicily with the title of king. In 1718, howeve he was obliged to exchange Sicily for Sardinia, again with the title of king, of the latter island this time He abdicated in 1730 in favour of his son Carlo Emanuele.

The latter for his aid to France in the War of the Polish Succession temporarily from 1734 to 1736 held the duchy of Milan, but was forced to relinquish it on the peace The War of the Austrian Succession added a little Piedmontese territory in 1748.

The succeeding king, Victor Amadeo III (1773-1796), was incapable and extravagant and Savoy fell an easy victim before the armies of the French Republic. The dynasty retired to Sardinia and returned to Piedmont only with the general peace in 1815.

VICTOR AMEDEO II AS DUKE OF SAVOY 1675-1730

1492   SCUDO BIANCO 1711
VICTOR. AM. II. - D.G. DVX SAB., bust R.
.PRIN. PEDE - REX. CYPRI., crowned and supported arms with 1711 below.

CARLO EMANUELE II AS KING OF SARDINIA 1730-1773

1493   SCUDO 1733-1735
CAR. EM. D.G. REX. SAR. CYP. ET IER., bust R with .*. below.
*DVX SAB. ET MON - TISF. PRINC. PED. * . divided date., crowned arms in elaborate frame

494   SCUDO OF 6 LIRE 1755-1758, 1763, 1765, 1769
CAR. EM. D.G. REX. SAR. CYP. ET. IER., bust L, date below.
DVX. SABAVD. ET. MONTISFER. PRINC. PEDEM. &., crowned arms in chain.

495   SCUDO SARDO 1768-1769
Similar to #1494 with head L.
DVX. SAB. ET. MONTISFER. PRINC. PED. &., crowned arms in chain.
Struck for Sardinia with the Sardinian arms.

VICTOR AMADEO III   1773-1796

496   SCUDO 1773
VIC. AM. D.G. REX. SAR. CYP. ET. IER., bust L, date below.
DVX. SABAVD. ET. MONTISFER. PRINC. PEDEM. &., crowned arms in chain.
A 1776 is also reported.

1497   SCUDO SARDO 1773
Similar to #1496 with head L.
Similar to #1495.

TUSCANY

WHEN the ancient Marquisate of Toscana broke up in 1114, most of the cities in the
state declared their independence and established republics. Florence surrendered
o the Imperial forces in 1530, and the Emperor and Pope agreed to convert the
epublic into a duchy and conferred the title of duke of Tuscany on Alessandro de
Iedici. In the following reign Siena was added and the duchy raised to a grand duchy.
he rule of the house of Medici is not distinguished for its benefits to Florence and
rt and life in the city declined. The last Medici duke died childless in 1737, and by a
revious arrangement the grand duchy passed to Francis, duke of Lorraine, husband of
Iaria Theresia, the Habsburg heiress. Francis ruled the duchy thru a regency and after
is accession never entered his domain. The state suffered a series of foreign regents
nd adventurers. On Francis' death in 1765 his younger son Peter Leopold succeeded
nd came to govern Tuscany in person.

A remarkable succession of reforms ensued, in government, taxation, agriculture,
he courts, punishments, army, and even, unsuccessfully in the long run, the Church.
ome of these were in advance of the times and not properly appreciated by those
enefiting.

When the grand duke became Holy Roman Emperor on the death of his brother
1790, after a brief regency he designated his second son, Ferdinand, a native Tuscan,
) succeed him in the duchy. Ferdinand was forced to flee in 1799 before the French
rmies, who after temporary reverses, were in firm control of the duchy in 1800.

The coins of Cosimo III and Gian Gastone are from the Livorno mint; those of
rancis II, Peter Leopold, and Ferdinand III from Pisa.

COSIMO III   1670-1723

498   TOLLERO 1701-1704
COSMVS. III. D(.)G(.) MAG. DVX. ETRVRIAE. VI.date., crowned bust R.
ET PATET . ET FAVET ., harbor scene.

499   PEZZA DELLA ROSA 1701, 1703, 1706
COSMVS. III. D.G. - M. DVX. ETRVRIAE.date, crowned Medici shield.
GRATIA OBVIA VLTIO QVAESTIA. LIBVRNI., rosebush.

1500   TOLLERO   1707-1708, 1711-1712, 1717, 1720, 1723

Similar to #1498 with uncrowned bust R.
ET PATET - ET FAVET., crown over stone gateway, FIDES below.
The 1708 and a variety of the 1707 have only M. for MAG.

1501   PEZZA DELLA ROSA   1706-1707, 1713, 1716, 1718

Similar to #1499 with higher, narrower crown.
Similar to #1499.

GIAN GASTONE   1723-1737

1502   TOLLERO   1723-1726

IOAN. GASTO. I. D.G. MAG. DVX. ETRVR. VII.date., bust R.
Similar to #1500 with .FIDES.

03   PEZZA DELLA ROSA   1726
IOAN. GASTO. I. D.G. - M. DVX. ETRVRIAE.1726., crowned Medici shield.
Similar to #1499.

FRANCIS II OF LORRAINE   1737-1765

504   TOLLERO   1747
FRANCISCVS.D.G.R.I.S.A.G. HIER. REX. LOTH. BAR. M.D. ETR., bust R with bird below.
.IN. TE. DOMI - NE. SPERAVI.; crowned double eagle with arms, PISIS - 1747 below.

505   TOLLERO   1747, 1758-1765
FRANCISCVS. D.G.R.I.S.A.G.H. REX. LOT. BAR. M.D. ETR, bust R with crossed axes below.
Similar to #1504 with larger, broader eagle and smaller arms.
The 1747 is in different style from the later dates and has the legend and mintmark of #1504.

N

1506   TOLLERO 1748

Legend similar to #1504 with bust like #1505.

.IN. TE. DOMINE - SPERAVI. - PISIS - MDCCXLVIII, crowned double eagle with arms.

1507   TOLLERO 1748-1750, 1753-1756, 1758

FRANCISCVS. D.G.R.I.S.A. - G.H. REX. LOT. BAR. M.D. ETR., bust R with bird below.
IN. TE. DOMINE - SPERAVI., crowned double eagle with arms, PISIS dividing date below.
A. A variety of the 1748 with the obverse inscription of #1504.

PETER LEOPOLD   1765-1790

1508   TALLERO 1765-1766

PETRVS LEOPOLDVS. D.G.P.R.H. ET. B.A.A.M.D. ETRVR. crossed pikes, bust R with L.
on bust.
DIRIGE DOMINE - GRESSVS MEOS., crowned thin oval arms with PISIS - date below.

509   TALLERO 1766

Similar to #1508 with or without L.S.
Similar to #1508 with wide ornate arms.

510   TALLERO 1766-1771

Similar to #1508 but bare necked bust with flowing hair.
Similar to #1509.
Most dates come with two spellings, ETRVR. or ETRVRIAE.

511   TALLERO 1767-1768

Similar to #1508 but armored bust L.
Similar to #1509.

1512 **TALLERO FOR THE LEVANT 1769**

P. LEOP. D.G.P.R.H. - ET B.A.A.M.D.E., armored bust R.
1769 X - IN TE - DOMINE - SPERAVI, crowned arms supported by two eagles.

1513 **TALLERO FOR THE LEVANT 1769, 1773-1774**

P. LEOP. D.G.P.R.H. ET - B.A.A.M.D. ETR., armored bust R with L.S.F. on arm,
Similar to #1512 with much smaller figures and letters.
The three dates differ in many details.

1514 **TALLERO 1771-1777**

P. LEOPOLDVS D.G.P.R.H. ET B.A.A.M.D. ETR., bust with flowing hair R.
Similar to #1508 with rectangular arms in order chain.
Many varieties. With initials: L.S.F., S.F., I.V., Z.V., I.Z.V., or I.VEBER. 1773-1775 also have
ETRVR. 1776-1777 also have ET.

15   TALLERO   1777-1782

P. LEOPOLDVS D.G.P.R.H. ET. B.A.A.M.D. ETR(VR).. small high collared bust R with bound hair.

Similar to #1514.

All dates have the spellings ETR. or ETRVR.

16   TALLERO   1783-1786

P. LEOPOLDVS. D.G. - P.R.H. ET. B.A.A.M.D. ETR., large high collared bust R.

Similar to #1514.

Many different varieties in spelling E, ET, ETR, or ETRVR, many divisions of obverse legend, two different busts on 1784 (one with initials A.C.F.) and on 1786, a new shield on the 1786, etc.

517   TALLERO   1785-1786

Similar to #1516, smaller bust with only a slight break in the legend.

Similar to #1514, shorter arms with thinner, more circular order chain.

The 1786 has both ETR. and ETRVR.

1518   TALLERO 1786-1787, 1789-1790

Similar to #1515, older bust R with unbroken legend.
Similar to #1517.
All dates have both ETR. and ETRVR. Two busts on the 1787, a long head and a round hea

1519   TALLERO 1790

LEOPOLDVS. II. D.G.R.I.S.A. GER. H. ET, B. REX. A.A.M.D. ETR., bust R with LS mono
gram and unicorn below.
DIRIGE DOMINE - GRESSVS MEOS, crowned double eagle with arms on breast, PISIS an
1790 below.

1520   TALLERO 1790

LEOPOLDVS. II. D.G.H. ET. B. REX. A.A.M.D.E., bust R with unicorn and monogram below
DIRIGE DOMINE - GRESSVS MEOS., crowned arms supported by two griffins, PISIS and
1790 below.

FERDINAND III 1790-1801

521 [149]   TALLERO 1791-1800

FERDINANDVS. III. D.G.P.R.H. ET. B.A.A.M.D. ETRVR., head R with monogram and unicorn below.
LEX TVA - VERITAS, crowned arms in order chain with PISIS and date below.
A. Variety of 1794-1795, 1797-1799 with ETR. B. Variety of 1791, 1799-1800 with order chain inside star tips.

VASTO

VASTO, 88 kilometers from Chieti in Abrizzo Citra, was the ancient Histonium. In 1460 the cit and castle were given to a member of the Avalo(s) family by Alphonso V of Aragon. Th d'Aquino title came from his wife. Don Cesare was created a prince of the Empire by Leopold I : 1704 with the mint privilege. He coined only in 1706–1707. In 1806 Vasto was incorporated int the Two Sicilies.

CESARE D'AVALOS D'AQUINO, MARCHESE DEL VASTO   1704-1729

1523   TALLERO 1706

*CAES. DAVALOS DE AQVINO DE ARAG. MAR. PIS ET VASTI D.G.S.R.I. PR., bust R.
DOMINVS REGIT ME. ANNO. 1706., crowned arms in elaborate frame.
Augsburg mint.

VENICE

7ENICE, built on a group of islands at the head of the Adriatic sea, instituted a
   republican government under a doge in the times of Charlemagne, and over the
.cceeding centuries, sometimes as a vassal state of the Byzantine Empire, grew into a
ealthy maritime power. When the Fourth Crusade occupied Constantinople in 1204
e Venetians took possession of numerous islands and lands in the Aegean and
.ack seas areas. Increased trade brought an increase in the number of wealthy fam-
es, who eventually seized the power from doge and people and turned Venice into
ι oligarchy. Long years of rivalry in the Levant and Black sea trade and mutual
predations with the Genoese followed. In 1380 Venice finally triumphed. The immedi-
ely succeeding period saw the gradual accretion of land on the mainland in what
me finally to be known as the Venetia. Such cities as Verona, Padua, Vicenza, Brescia,
ergamo, Crema, and Rovigo came temporarily or permanently under her control. The
ll of Constantinople in 1453 to the Ottoman Turks marks the beginning of a steady
ss, except for the possession of Cyprus acquired in 1488, of her eastern territories.
1486 when the Cape route to the Indies was discovered, no possibility of Venetian
»minance remained. The decline though slow was continuous, illuminated by the
illiant days of her great art when Titian, Tintoretto, and Veronese decorated her
.urches and palaces. Luxurious life continued and Venice became the most famous
easure city of Europe.

On May 12, 1797 the last doge abdicated in the face of hopeless resistance to the
apoleonic armies. After a short lived republic Venice was handed over to Austria,
ider whose domination, except for a French period between 1806 and 1814, she re-
ained until 1866.

Since the designs on both sides of all the Venetian denominations, scudo, ducatone,
icato, leone for the Levant, and the two talleros, remained constant with only a change
the doge's name and a few minor variations, they are being illustrated only once.
. the description of the coinage under the various doges only the reverse legend with
e doge's name, the initials of the mintmaster, and any significant variations are
escribed. For a complete picture of a coin, reference will have to be made to the
ustration or to the inclusive descriptions given under #1524-1528, 1552, and 1563.

SCUDO

DUCATONE

DUCATO

LEONE FOR THE LEVANT

ALVISE MOCENIGO II   1700-1709

1524   SCUDO

* SANCTVS * MARCVS * VENET *, arms in frame, * 140 * in exergue.

* ALOYSIVS * MOCENICO * DVX * VENET * with B*C or P*B, floriated ornate cross in beaded border.

525 DUCATONE
* MEMOR * ERO * TVI * IVSTINA * VIR(G)(O)(.) * 124, standing saint with seascape in the background.
*S*M*V* ALOY ✧ MOCENICO * D(VX)*, winged lion with saint kneeling before banner, in exergue *B*C* or B*P*

526 2 DUCATI

527 DUCATO
DVCATVS * VENETVS * , lion of St. Marks with tablet, rosettes below.
*S*M*V* ALOY:(*) MOCENI(C)(O) * D(V) *, seated and kneeling figures with banner, in exergue *B✧C*, *P✧M*, G*T*S*, or *P✧B*

528 LEONE FOR THE LEVANT
FIDES. ET. * VICTORIA *, rearing lion of St. Marks with cross.
S*M✧ VENETV * - ALOY* MOCEN *, standing and kneeling figures with DVX beside staff and *B*C* below.

GIOVANNI CORNER II   1709-1722

529 2 SCUDI

530 SCUDO
✧ IOANNES ✧ CORNELIO * DVX * VEN * with initials F A P or A M

531 DUCATONE
*S*M*V IOAN * CORNEL * D ✧ with initials F A P

532 2 DUCATI

533 DUCATO
*S*M*V* IOAN * CORNEL(I0) ✧ D(VX) * with F A P, A M, M B, or D D

534 LEONE FOR THE LEVANT
S*M* VENET* - IOAN * CORNEL ✧ with A M

ALVISE MOCENIGO III   1722-1732

535 SCUDO
✧ ALOYSIVS * MOCENICO ✧ DVX * VEN * with initials V Q

536 DUCATONE
*S*M*V* ALOY ✧ MOCENI * D ✧ with initials V Q

537 DUCATO
*S*M✧V* ALOY * MOCENICO * D ✧ with initials V Q

CARLO RUZZINI   1732-1735

538 SCUDO
* CAROLVS ✧ RVZINI ✧ DVX ✧ VENETIAR ✧ with initials B V

539 DUCATONE
*S*M*V* CAROLVS * RVZINI * D * with initials B V
The obverse has VIRG.

540 DUCATO
*S✧M*V* CAROLVS * RVZINI * D ✧ with initials B V or Z Z

ALVISE PISANI   1735-1741

1541   SCUDO
* ALOYSIVS * PISANI * DVX * VENETIAR * with initials Z F

1542   DUCATONE
*S*M*V* ALOYSIVS ⁕ PISANI * D ⁕ with initials Z F or M S
The obverse has VIRGO.

A1543   2 DUCATI

1543   DUCATO
*S*M*V* ALOYSIVS * PISANI ⁕ D * with initials Z F or M S

PIETRO GRIMANI   1741-1752

1544   SCUDO
* PETRVS * GRIMANI ⁕ DVX ⁕ VENÉTIAR ⁕ with initials F P

1545   DUCATONE
*S*M*V* PETRVS * GRIMANI * D * with initials F P

1546   2 DUCATI

1547   DUCATO
*S*M*V* PETRVS ⁕ GRIMANI * D ⁕ with initials F P, F A F, or A B

FRANCESCO LOREDAN   1752-1762

1548   SCUDO
* FRANC * LAVREDANO * DVX ⁕ VENETIAR * with initials G A C

1549   DUCATONE
*S*M*V* FRANC ⁕ LAVREDANO ⁕ DVX ⁕ with initials G A C

1550   2 DUCATI

1551   DUCATO
*S*M*V* FRANC * LAVREDANO ⁕ D * with initials G A C or S B

1552   TALLERO 1756, 1760, 1761
RESPUBLICA VENETA, bust of the Republic R.
FRANC: LAUREDANO DUCE. date, lion in frame.
Three varieties of bust.

MARCO FOSCARINI 1762-1763

A1553 2 SCUDI

1553 SCUDO
* MARCVS * FOSCARENVS * DVX * VENETIAR * with initials Z D

1554 DUCATONE
*S*M*V* M * FOSCARENVS * DVX * with initials Z D

1555 DUCATO
*S*M*V* MARC * FOSCARENVS * D * with initials Z D or Z M

1556 TALLERO 1762
MARCO FOSCARENO DUCE 1762, similar to #1552.

ALVISE MOĆENIGO IV 1763-1778

1557 SCUDO
* ALOYSIVS * MOCENICO * DVX * VENETIAR * with initials D G or M A T

1558 2 DUCATONE

1559 DUCATONE
*S*M*V* ALOY: MOCENICO * D(VX) * with initials D G or B C

1560 2 DUCATI

1561 DUCATO
*S*M*V* ALOY: MOCENICO * D * with initials D G, B C, R B P, G A F, G P, G M B, L B, V V, A M P, P D, V S

1562 TALLERO 1764, 1766
*ALOI(Y)SII MOCENICO DUCE date * similar to #1552.

1563 TALLERO 1768-1769
RESPUBLICA — VENETA flower *, new bust R.
*ALOYSIO MOCENICO DUCE * flower *, winged lion seated with book, * date * below and .A. - .S. on base.

PAOLO RENIER 1779-1789

1564 SCUDO
* PAULUS * RAINERIUS * DVX * VENETIAR * with initials L A F

1565 DUCATONE
* S.M.V. PAVL. RAINERIVS. D(VX). with initials L A F or B C

1566 2 DUCATI

1567 DUCATO
* S.M.V. PAVL. RAINERIVS. D. with initials, L A F, B C, R B, F D, A O, A B, F R, G F, A F, A C, A D

1568 TALLERO 1781, 1784-1788
*PAULO RAINERIO DUCE * flower *, similar to #1563.

LODOVICO MANIN   1789-1797

1569   2 SCUDI

1570   SCUDO
* LUDOVICUS. MANIN * DVX * VENETIAR * with initials G F

1571   2 DUCATONE

1572   DUCATONE
*S.M.V. LUDOV(I). MANIN. DVX * with initials G F

1573   2 DUCATI

1574   DUCATO
*S.M.V. LUDOVI. MANIN. D. with initials G F, A C, F B, A D, A Z, D C

1575   TALLERO   1789-1792, 1794-1797
*LUDOVICO MANIN DUCE * flower *, similar to #1563.

REPUBLIC   1797-1798

1576   10 LIRE 1797

LIBERTA - EGUAGLIANZA., Liberty standing by fasces with liberty pole and cap, below ZECCA.V. and A.S.
ANNO. I. DELLA LIBERTA ITALIANA. 1797 *, in wreath * / LIRE / DIECI / VENETE / .*
A. variety with reverse of #1577.

1577   10 LIRE 1797

Similar to #1576 with no rosette before the legend and Z * V under the figure.
Similar to #1576 with no rosettes or periods and with 1797 below wreath.

LIECHTENSTEIN

THE counts of Liechtenstein, on the Austro-Swiss border, though of ancient lineage were undistinguished until the 17th century. Count Carl, an Imperialist general, as created duke of Troppau in 1614, prince in 1618, and duke of Jägerndorf in Silesia 1623. He was also given coining privileges. Liechtenstein proper was formed in 1719 y the union of the lordship of Schellenberg and the county of Vaduz on the Swiss order. Seventeenth century pieces were coined for Troppau and Jägerndorf; those in ghteenth century for Liechtenstein.

JOSEPH JOHANN ADAM   (1721-1732)

578   TALER 1728, 1729

IOS: IO: AD: D:G:S:R:I:P.& GUB: DOM: DE LIECHTENSTEIN, bust R.
OPP: & CARN: DUX. C. RITB: GRAN: HISP: P: CLAS: S.C.M. INT. CONS: date, crowned and mantled arms.

JOSEPH WENZEL   (1748-1772)

579   TALER 1758

IOS. WENC. D.G.S.R.I.PR & GUB. DOM. DE LIECHTENSTEIN., bust R.
OPP. & CARN. DUX COM. RITTB. S.C.M. CONS. INT. & CAMPI=MARESCHAL, crowned and supported arms with 17 - 58 below.
Three obverse and two reverse dies.

FRANZ JOSEPH I   (1772-1781)

1580   TALER   1778

FRANC. IOS. D.G.S.R.I.PR. & GUB. DOM. DE LIECHTENSTEIN., bust R with F.W. below.

OPP. & CARN. DUX. COM. RITTB. S.C.M. CONS. INT.AUR. VELLERIS EQUES. 1778 crowned arms in chain.

LIEGE

THE bishopric of Liege was constituted under that title about 930 replacing an older see. It lay along the Meuse, Sambre, and Ourche rivers in what is modern Belgium, dividing completely the two parts of the Austro-Spanish Netherlands. It increased in size over the years by the incorporation of such lands as the duchy of Bouillon, the marquisate of Franchimont, the county of Hoorn, and part of the county of Looz, until at the time of its secularization in 1802 it contained 2,200 square miles and had a population of some 233,000 people.

JOSEPH CLEMENS, DUKE OF BAVARIA   1694-1723

1581   PATAGON 1716

IOS. CLE. D.G. ARCH. COL. S.R.I.P. EL. B.D., bust R with 1716 below.

E. P. LE. - D. BUL. - C.L. HO. - M. FRA, center shield with four around in the angles of crossed sword and mitre.

SEDE VACANTE   1723-1724

1582   DOUBLE PATAGON 1724

1583   PATAGON 1724

* MONETA.NOVA. CAPLI. LEOD.˙SEDE. VACANTE, crowned and mantled arms with 17 - 24 above.

* S. LAMBERTUS. PATRONUS. LEODIENSIS.*, bust L.

1584   PATAGON 1724

Similar to #1582, another shaped shield without mantle or date.
Similar to #1582 with 1724 at top.

1585   PATAGON 1724

Similar to #1584 with 17 - 24 at sides.
Similar to #1583.

SEDE VACANTE   1744

1586   DOUBLE PATAGON 1744

1587   PATAGON 1744

Similar to #1583, larger cap and differently shaped arms with no date.
Similar to #1584 with 1744 at top.

SEDE VACANTE   1763

588   **PATAGON   1763**
Similar to #1587 with oval shaped arms.
Similar to #1587 with date 1763.

SEDE VACANTE   1771

1589   **PATAGON   1771**
Similar to #1588.
Similar to #1587 with date 1771.

SEDE VACANTE   1784

1590   **PATAGON   1784**
Similar to #1588.
Similar to #1587 with date 1784.

SEDE VACANTE 1792

1591 PATAGON 1792

Similar to #1588.
Similar to #1587 with date 1792.

LUXEMBURG

THE county of Luxemburg, situated on the Franco-German-Belgian border, was
part of the Frankish kingdom and then the Carolingian Empire before acquiring
its own counts in 963. Another line of rulers originated in 1226. To this house belonged
several emperors and kings of Bohemia. The county was raised to a duchy in 1354.
This line, too, disappeared and Luxemburg passed to Burgundy in 1444, to the Habsburgs in 1477, to Spain in 1555, and back to Austria in 1713. The only crown size piece
of the eighteenth century was struck in 1795 by General Bender as a necessity piece
while the French were besieging the city of Luxemburg.

1592   72 ASSES (SOLS) 1795

AD / USUM / LUXEMBURGI / CC VALLATI / .1795. /
LXXII / ASSES / 13 between branches.

MALTA

THE Order of the Knights of St. John of Jerusalem, known later as the Knights of Rhodes and the Knights of Malta, was the outgrowth of a hospital or hospice for Christians in the Holy Land. Founded about 1087 by Gerard, head of the hospital, the Order soon embraced members from most European Christian countries. Warfare in the Holy Land continued, and the Knights as they grew more powerful and less ecclesiastic took on the nature of a military order. They remained with headquarters in Jerusalem until the fall of the Latin kingdom there in 1291; then they removed to Cyprus.

About 1309 they were given the island of Rhodes, one of the Dodecanese off the coast of Turkey. As the religious fervor of the Middle Ages declined, the Order became more and more politically and commercially involved. For two centuries their naval power held back the Mohammedans, but in 1523 after a siege of the island by Suleiman the Magnificent the Knights capitulated and withdrew to Crete. In 1530 Charles V granted them the island of Malta and the fortress of Tripoli in Africa. In 1551 the latter was abandoned and all power concentrated in Malta.

The military glories of the sieges of St. Elmo and St. Angelo and the battle of Lepanto were followed in the 17th century by a period of decline with internal dissensions and quarrels. The wealth of the Order had increased enormously and its membership had grown more aristocratic. The buildings on the island were magnificent but the relations with the Maltese people worsened through neglect and imperiousness.

During its last century of occupation in Malta and its last century of significance the story is one of gradual decay. Antony Manoel de Vilhena (1722-1736) of Castile suppressed a serious rising of Turkish slaves and prisoners. Raymond Despuig (1736-1741), formerly Baliff of Majorca, enjoyed a relatively calm reign. Emmanuel Pinto (1741-1773), a Portuguese, thwarted another serious conspiracy in 1749 and secured some further victories over the Turks. Under his successor, Francis Ximenez de Texada (1773-1775), Grand Prior of Navarre, disorders and discontent among the Maltese arose. The Grand Master was arrogant and obstinate, and during a revolt in 1775 the Bishop of Malta had to be called in to restore order. Emmanuel, Prince de Rohan (1775-1797), a Frenchman, introduced reforms and restored good relations. He was an able and energetic ruler who governed a flourishing Order. The last Grand Master in Malta, Ferdinand Hompesch (1797-1799), was a German of no ability and little willpower. The French had already planned the destruction of Malta, the Order having been suppressed in France in 1792. And in June of 1798, partly through treachery, Napoleon occupied the island, and the practical connection of the Order with their home for 250 years ceased.

The currency parallels that of the Kingdom of Naples and Sicily, the nearest European nation.

ANTONY MANOEL DE VILHENA   1722-1736

1593   2 SCUDI 1723
F.D. AN: MANOEL* DE* VILHENA*, bust R in border.
M. MAGIS: HOS: ET S. SEPVL: HIERVSALEM 1723.*., two oval shields crowned separating S - 2
There are a great many varieties.

594   2 SCUDI 1724

Legend similar to #1593 but begins at the top. Division before or after the DE

M. MAGIS(TER): HOS(P): ET S. S(EPVL): HIERVS(A) (L) (EM)*1.7.2.4***, crowned arms similar to #1593.

Many dies, with or without stars in legend; reverse legend broken or unbroken at top and bottom.

1595   2 SCUDI 1724

Similar to #1594 without inner band.

M. MAGISTER HOSP:* - *ET S.S. HIERVS: 1724, larger crowned arms without inner border. Several dies as on #1594.

1596   2 SCUDI 1725

Similar to #1595 without stars at the ends of the legend.

Similar to #1595 with legend unbroken at the bottom.

Many varieties. Spelling HOS(P). and HIERVS(A)(LE).

1597   2 SCUDI 1728

Similar to #1594 with or without inner border.
Similar to #1596 with HIERVS(A).
Several dies.

RAYMOND DESPUIG   1736-1741

1598   2 SCUDI 1738

F. (D). RAIMVN(DVS). DESPVYG M.M.H.H., bust R with or without border.
Crowned arms in scroll dividing 17 - 38 above and S - 2 at the sides or below the scroll.
Many varieties. One with a fancy shaped shield.

EMMANUEL PINTO   1741-1773

1599   2 SCUDI 1741

F. (D). EMMA - NVEL PINTO, bust L.
M.M.H. ET S. - SEP. HIER., crowned arms in scroll. 17 - 41 above.
Several varieties. A. With solid obverse legend. B. With arms in frame shaped like that on #1600.

1600   30 TARI 1756-1759, 1761

F. EMMANVEL PINTO - M.M.H.S.S.date, crowned arms.
NON - SVRREXIT MAIOR, St. John the Baptist standing with banner, lamb at R, in exergue T.XXX
Several different shapes for the shield. The position of the Baptist varies with different banners and arm raised or lowered. The spacing of the reverse legend varies. A. With obverse of #1601.

1601   30 TARI 1761

Similar to #1600 with legend unbroken at the bottom.
Similar to #1600 with lamb standing.
Several varieties. A. One with lamb reclining. B. With branches behind arms.

1602   30 TARI 1761

Similar to #1601.
.NON. SVRREXIT. - MAIOR., the Baptist with small banner looking R.

1603   2 SCUDI 1764

F. EMMANVEL PINTO M.M.H.S.S.. bust L.
Two heart shaped shields crowned. 17 - 64 above. S. - 2 below.
Several varieties.

1604   30 TARI 1768

F. EMMANUEL PIN: - TO M.M.H.S.S.1768, crowned arms.
Similar to #1600, the Baptist faces L with banner in left hand.

FRANCIS XIMENEZ DE TEXADA   1773-1775

1605   2 SCUDI 1773-1774

FR. D. FRANCISCVS XIMENEZ DE TEXADA .. date., bust R.
Crowned shields in sprays separating S. - .2 above.
Varieties with garlands separating shields and one with J774.

EMMANUEL DE ROHAN   1775-1797

1606   30 TARI 1777
F. EMMANUEL DE ROHAN. M.M.H.S.S., bust R.
Two shields crowned separating .T. - .XXX above and .1-77-7. below.

1607   30 TARI 1779
F. EMMANUEL DE - ROHAN M.M., bust R.
.HOSPITA(LIS) ET S. - SEP(UL). HIERUS(AL). 17 - 79, crowned arms on eagle separating
.T. - .XXX above.

1608   30 TARI 1781, 1785, 1789-1790
Similar to #1607.
HOSPITA. ET S. - SEP. HIERUS. date, crowned shield on eagle separating T. - 30
Several varieties.

1609   30 TARI   1789-1790, 1795-1796
Similar to #1607 with new bust R.
Similar to #1608.
All dates with or without small eagle under bust.

1610   2 SCUDI   1796
Similar to #1609.
Crowned shield in sprays. 17 - 96 above. S. - 2 below.
Four varieties.

FERDINAND HOMPESCH   1797-1799

1611   30 TARI   1798
F. FERDINANDVS - HOMPESCH M.M., bust L.
HOSPITAL. ET - S. SEP. HIER. 17 - 98, crowned double eagle with arms on breast separating T. - 30 above.
Variety with small cross under bust. The varieties with a dot under the bust or before the face were supposedly struck later by the French during their occupation of the island.

MONACO

THE sovereign principality of Monaco, six square miles on the Mediterranean entirely surrounded now by France, came under control of the Genoese family of the Grimaldi in 968. French influence usually dominated though at times Italian and Spanish forces were in the ascendant. The only scudos of the eighteenth century were issued by Antonio, whose death in 1731 brought to an end the male line of the Grimaldis.

ANTONIO I   1701-1731

612   SCUDO 1707, 1708, 1715

.ANT. I. D. G. PRIN. MONOEGI., bust R.
AVXILIVM. MEVM. A. DOMINO. date., crowned arms.
The dates all differ slightly. There are 3 varieties of the 1707, one of the 1708, and two of the 1715.

POLAND

THE tribes along the Vistula river in what is modern Poland were converted t Christianity in the 10th century. Boleslaus I (992-1025) built up a huge realm an assumed the royal title. His successors battled Tatars, Bohemians, Lithuanians, an Cossacks to maintain their position. Civil war raged after the death of Louis the Grea of Poland and Hungary in 1382, but was settled finally when Louis's daughter Jadwig was recognized as queen of Poland and married to Jagello, duke of Lithuania, wh became king. The Lithuanian line came to an end at the death of Sigismund II in 157: As the Polish throne was elective, the ruler being chosen by the diet, a series of foreig born rulers followed. In 1668 a Swedish line became extinct, and a period of politica corruption followed, abetted by the stupid "liberum veto," which required unanimou consent to pass any law in the diet.

Michael Wisniowiecki (1669-1674), the next choice, was in Habsburg pay, and Joh III Sobieski (1674-1696), though the hero of the great defense of Vienna against th Turks in 1683, was overly influenced by French intrigues.

The successful candidate among the eighteen would-be successors of the late kin was Friedrich August, elector of Saxony, who was crowned Augustus II in 1697. Th great northern war involving Sweden, Denmark, and Russia completely despoile Poland, and during the period of Swedish victory Charles XII of Sweden maintaine Stanislaus Leszczynski on the throne of Poland as king (1704-1709). The end of th war saw Poland a ruined state, and at his death in 1733 Augustus had in no wa succeeded in compensating his adopted country for its great losses.

Stanislaus Leszczynski, who had become father-in-law of the French king Louis X and prospective duke of Lorraine, was reelected king with French aid, but Polish mal contents with Russian assistance drove him out and substituted the son of Augustu II, Friedrich August of Saxony, who became Augustus III (1733-1763). His reig marks a period of conflict between the Czartoryskis, a leading Polish family patriotic ally desirous of reforming and strengthening Poland, to whom the king left the man agement of the kingdom, and other noble Polish families jealous of their powers Nothing was accomplished, and by the end of the reign all Poland's enemies were prin cipally concerned with maintaining the anarchical state then existing in the nation.

Russia and Prussia had determined on Stanislaus II Poniatowski (1764-1795) a the best agent available to carry out their wishes and he was duly elected. Parliament actually browbeaten by Russian troops in the capital, gave in to every regulation t weaken Poland, and the beginning of the end approached. Prussia and Austria, fearfu of Russia's stranglehold on Poland, finally came to terms with her, and in 1772 cam the first partition wherein all three powers helped themselves to a slice of Polis territory. One-fourth of the land and one-fifth of the population were lost. Under th shock of the partition and after the death of Friedrich the Great in 1786, Poland seeme for a few years to steady and grow stronger. In 1791 by devious means a moder constitution changing the state into a liberal hereditary monarchy was pushed throug Russian troops invaded under the instigation of Polish conspirators, who formed confederation at Targowica in the Ukraine aimed at overthrowing the new constitution Prussia backed out of the her commitments to the new state, and the little Polish arm faced the Russian invaders bravely and successfully for a few months. But the gov ernment and the king, dubious of any prolonged success, capitulated and the old con stitution was restored. The liberals fled abroad. Russian troops occupied much o eastern Poland, and the Prussians afraid of Russia's swallowing the whole countr marched into Great Poland. The second partition of 1793 followed with Prussia an Russia dividing the spoils. One-third only remained. The Polish patriotic governmen in Leipzig fought on. Kosciuszko proclaimed a national insurrection at Cracow in 1794 Initial successes were turned into eventual defeats by internal dissension and th masses of Russian soldiers. The three neighboring powers in their greed divided wha remained of the territory, and Poland as a nation ceased to exist in 1796.

AUGUSTUS II   1697-1704, 1709-1733

613   BEICHINGER TALER (8 FLORINS) 1702
*AUGUSTUS. II. D.G. REX. POL. M.D. LIT. D. SAX. I.C.M.A. & W., four crowned A's and
four II's around central cross.
SAC. ROM. IMP. ARCHIM. ET. ELECT.1702., crowned arms in decorative frame.

614   REICHSTALER 1702
AUGUSTUS. II. D.G. REX. POLON. M. DUX. LIT., crowned bust R.
*DUX. SAX. I.C.M.A.&.W. ELECT. 1702., crowned arms with crowned monograms at sides.
Below E P - H.

615   TALER 1702
*AUGUSTUS. II. D.G. REX. POLONIARUM., crowned Andreas cross with draped band of the
Order of the Elephant; crowned AS at R and L.
DUX. SAX. I.C.M.A.&.W. ELECT. 17 - 02, crowned Saxony-Poland arms with Order of the
Elephant.

1616   TALAR (32 GROSZ) N.D. [1733]
Crowned AR with 32.gr. below.
Six-winged butterfly.
On the death of the king.

AUGUSTUS III   1733-1763

1617   TALAR 1753-1756
D:G: AVGVSTVS. III. REX. POLONIARUM., crowned bust R.
SAC. ROM. IMP. ARCHIM. ET ELECT. date, crowned arms in sprays with E.D.C. below.
Many varieties in size of the head and lettering, style of crowns, king's robes, and palm spray.
The 1762 is a pattern.

STANISLAUS PONIATOWSKI   1764-1795

1618   TALAR 1766
STANISLAUS AUGUSTUS D.G. REX. POL. M.D. LITHU., bust R.
X EX MARCA PURA - COLONIEN.1766, crowned arms in sprays, F.-S. below.

19   TALAR 1768-1770, 1772-1782

STANISLAUS AUGUSTUS D.G. REX POL. M.D. LITH. or LITU., head R.
Similar to #1618.
Initials on 1768-1772 I.S. ; 1772-1774 A.P. ; 1775-1782 E.B.

20   TALAR 1783-1785

STANISLAUS AUGUSTUS D.G. REX. POLON. M.D. LITUAN., new head R.
Similar to last dates of #1619 with E. - B.

21   TALAR 1788, 1792

Similar to #1620, new head R.
10 7/16 EX MARCA PURA - COLONIENS:date., crowned arms in sprays with E. - B. below.

Q

1622   TARGOWICA TALAR 1793

GRATITUDO CONCIVIBUS EXEMPLUM POSTERITATI. In center in 9 lines: CIVIBU
QUORUM PIETAS / CONIURATIONE DIE III / MAI. MDCCXCI OBRUTAM /
DELETAM LIBERTA / TE POLONA TUERI / CONABATUR RESPU / BLICA RESU
GENS in oak wreath.

10 7/16 EX MARCA PURA COLONIENSI. 1793.*. In center in 6 lines: DECRET(
REIPUBLICAE NEXU / CONFEDERATIONIS IUNCTAE / DIE V. XBRIS MDCCXC
STANISLAO AUGUSTO / REGNANTE.

1623   TALAR 1794-1795

STANISLAUS AUGUSTUS D.G. REX. POLON: M.D. LIT., head R.

14 1/12 EX MARCA PUR: - COLONIENS:date., crowned arms in sprays with 6. - ZL. bel

COURLAND (KURLAND)

(OURLAND, comprising parts of modern Latvia and Lithuania, came under the
influence of the Teutonic Knights and finally in 1561 under Polish protection. In
at year the Grand Master of the Order, Gotthard Kettler, ceded the lands of the
vonian Order to Poland, but retained possession of the duchies of Courland and
migalia as fiefs of Poland. In 1562 he assumed the title of duke of Courland and
migalia, which remained in the family until its extinction in 1737.

At that time the Czarina Anna of Russia, who was the widow of an earlier Kettler
ke, put pressure on the Estates of the duchy and had her favorite, Ernst Johann
ron, a one-time groom of another earlier Kettler duke, elected to the vacant position.
s fortunes fell on the death of the Czarina. He was arrested, tried, sentenced to be
ecuted, banished to Siberia, and finally released under surveillance. In 1762 the
arina Catherine II restored him to his title and duchy. He abdicated in 1769 and
as succeeeded by his son Peter (born 1724). Peter reigned through the troublesome
mes of the partitions of Poland, and at the final one in 1795 the duchy passed com-
etely under Russian sovereignty and the duke abdicated in favor of the Czarina and
tired to his German estates.

PETER BIRON   1769-1795

624   TALER 1780
D.G. PETRUS IN LIV. CURL. ET SEMGAL. DUX, head R.
MON. NOVA ARG. DUC. CURL. AD NORMAM TAL. ALB. 1780, crowned arms of Poland
and Lithuania.

PORTUGAL

BY 1280 modern Portugal had taken shape. The monarchy, after its firm establis§ ment, expanded during the age of discoveries until a world-wide empire was create The Aviz dynasty died out in 1580, and for sixty years the kings of Spain were al§ kings of Portugal. When Portuguese independence was reestablished in 1640, Joh duke of Braganza, was chosen king to found a new dynasty. The opening of th 18th century saw the signing of a treaty in 1703 with England, which was to ceme§ close Anglo-Portuguese relations thruout the century. Gold poured in from Braz and had the country had wise rulers, it could have prospered tremendously. Cleric and foreign influence, however, dominated, and not until the ministry of the marqu§ of Pombal (1750-1777) did a truly national and beneficial policy develop. The famo§ Lisbon earthquake occurred in 1755. Pombal was dismissed in 1777 at the accessio of the new queen, Maria I, who was married to her uncle Pedro III, the king consor He died in 1786, and when the queen went insane in 1788, the country was governe by her son Don John, who assumed the official regency only in 1799.

PEDRO II   1681-1706

1625   CRUZADO NOVO 1702
PETRVS. II. D. G. REX. PORTVG., crowned arms with *400* at left and *1702* at right. .*.IN * HOC * SIGNO * VINCES, cross with P's in angles.

627   CRUZADO NOVO   1703-1706

PETRVS. II. D. G. PORT. ET. ALG. REX, similar to #1626 with legend broken at the top.
Similar to #1626.
The crown varies particularly on the 1706.

JOHN V   1706-1750

628   CRUZADO NOVO   1706-1708, 1717, 1750

IOANNES. V. D. G. PORT. ET. ALG. REX, crowned arms with *400* at left and * date *
at right.
Similar to #1626.
Some difference in the crowns. The 1750 comes with 4 or 5 supports.

JOSE I   1750-1777

629   CRUZADO NOVO   1762-1763, 1766

IOSEPHUS. I. D. G. PORT. ET. ALG. REX, similar to #1628.
Similar to #1626.

1630 **CRUZADO NOVO 1762-1763, 1766, 1768, 1774-1775**
Similar to #1629 with JOSEPHUS.
Similar to #1626.

MARIA AND PEDRO III   1777-1786

1631 **CRUZADO NOVO 1778-1782, 1784-1785**
MARIA. I. ET. PETRUS. III. D. G. PORT. ET. ALG. REGES, similar to #1628,
Similar to #1626.

MARIA I   1786-1816

1632 **CRUZADO NOVO 1786, 1788, 1792-1799**
MARIA. I. D. G. PORT. ET. ALG. REGINA, similar to #1628.
Similar to #1626.

JOHN AS PRINCE REGENT   1799-1816

₃33 [259]   CRUZADO NOVO   1799-1800

JOANNES. D. G. P. PORTUGALIAE ET. ALG., similar to #1628.
Similar to #1626.

RAGUSA

RAGUSA, a city in Dalmatia on the eastern coast of the Adriatic, was establish in the 7th century. In 1205 it acknowledged Venetian sovereignty. An oligarc government under a rector was constituted in 1358, and Hungarian overlordship reconized from 1358 to 1526. It flourished as a rich mercantile and trading center. As free republic after 1526 it had a famous literary renaissance, which came to an e with the disastrous earthquake of 1667, which leveled much of the city. Its 18 century history, like that of Venice, is one of steady decline. In 1814 it was annex to Austria. San Biagio was the patron saint of the city.

1635   TALLERO OF ST. BIAGIO 1725
   .DIVINA. - .PER. TE. OPE., large bust R separating S - B.
   DVCAT. ET. SEM . . . - . . . REIP. RHAC., crowned arms dividing 17 - 25.

1636   TALLERO OF ST. BIAGIO 1725, 1730-1731, 1733-1736, 1738, 1743, 1747
   .DIVINA. PER. - .TE. OPE., smaller bust R dividing S - B.
   .DVCAT. ET. SEM. - .REIP. RHAC. date., crowned arms.
   Many varieties.

37 TALLERO RETTORALE 1738, 1743-1748

.RECTOR. REIP. - RHACVSIN., large bust L.
Similar to #1636.
Many varieties in bust, frame for arms, spelling, etc.

338 TALLERO RETTORALE 1751

ET. PRAESIDIVM. - ET. DECVS. 1751, St. Biagio kneeling to L, below the city and .S.B.P.R.RH.
COELI. REGINA. - RP. RHAC PATRONA, Virgin on clouds.
The status of this taler is doubtful.

639 TALLERO 1751-1779

RECTOR. RE(I)(P). - .RHACVSIN., bust L.
DVCAT. ET. SEM. - REIP. RAC. (RACV) or (RHAC) or (RHAG.) date, crowned arms, with initials G.B., D-M, or G.A. below.
Many varieties in bust, shield decoration, size of lettering and dates, etc.

1640   LIBERTINA OF 2 DUCATS 1791

RESPVBL. - RHACVS., female bust R with G.A. below.
DVCE. DEO - FIDE. ET. IVST, crowned arms with G 17 - 91 A below.

1641   LIBERTINA OF 2 DUCATS 1792-1795

Similar to #1640 with another bust and RHACVS. or RHACVSI.
Similar to #1640 with crowned frame with LI / BER / TAS in sprays.

RUSSIA

URING the early 13th century Russia was overrun by Mongol hordes, and the Russian princes were forced to pay tribute to the Tartar Khans. By the end of the th century Tartar domination was at an end, but Russia remained isolated from the st of Europe maintaining many oriental customs of the old way of life.

In 1613 the Romanoff dynasty in the person of Michael Feodorovich came to the rone. Michael's grandson Peter was born in 1672 and succeeded his brother in 1676, t not until 1689 did he acquire complete sovereignty. Determined to bring his country reast of western civilization, Peter himself visited a number of European countries nd brought back many ideas and samples of commerce and trade. Russians were sent broad to be trained in useful occupations. Dynastic revolts and struggles to modernize e habits and apparel of the naturally conservative Russian populace occupied the zar's attention, and many reforms were introduced.. Territorial expansion occurred the regions of the Caspian and the Baltic; on the latter Peter built a new capital, t. Petersburg, in 1703.

The chaotic currency of his father's reign was systematized, and Peter began a niform coinage in all metals, with mints in Moscow and after 1724 in St. Petersburg. he first silver ruble appeared in 1704.

Since Peter had named no successor, at his death in 1725 his second wife Catherine, rmerly a Lithuanian servant, was proclaimed Empress, with the power actually in e hands of Menshikov, one of Peter's officials. Catherine died in 1727 and Peter's randson, Peter II, a boy of twelve, succeeded to the throne with Menshikov still in ower until his exile the next year when the Supreme Secret Council took over all ffairs of state.

Peter's II's death in 1729 brought to the throne the widowed duchess of Courland, nna, a niece of Peter the Great. The Empress was incompetent and the real ruler of ussia was her favorite Biron, who earned the hatred of most patriotic Russians. Anna ied in 1740 after appointing Biron as regent for her successor, a baby Ivan, great randson of Peter the Great's brother Ivan. Popular indignation was such that the mperial Guard exiled Biron to Siberia and appointed the child's mother as regent. his arrangement also proved unsatisfactory, and the Guard again exiled the Regent nd chose Elisabeth, Peter the Great's daughter as ruler. The child Ivan was put in rison, where he died 23 years later.

Elisabeth's reign, under the guidance of her minister Shuvalov, saw territorial xpansion in Finland at the expense of the Swedes, and military successes against rederick the Great of Prussia. Elisabeth brought her nephew, Peter of Schleswig-Iolstein, son of her sister Anna, to St. Petersburg and named him her successor. At er death in 1762, he ascended the throne as Peter III and immediately began to everse many of his predecessor's policies. His unsound mentality and his great admiraion of things German prompted the Imperial Guard in June of 1762 to arrest him and roclaim his wife ruler. He died a short time later.

Peter had married Sophia Augusta, princess of Anhalt-Zerbst, who had taken the ame of Catherine when she was baptized into the Greek Orthodox faith. A very ntelligent woman, she continued and extended many of the projects of Peter the Great. The three partitions of Poland occurred during her reign, and the country's boundaries were considerably extended as Russia developed into a European power.

Her death in 1796 brought her son Paul to the throne. His hatred of his mother spurred him to reverse many of her policies, and his cruel, suspicious nature quickly alienated most of the people surrounding him. In 1801 he was strangled by a group of army officers.

PETER THE GREAT   1689-1725

1642   RUBLE 1704-1705

(Czar Peter Alexievitch, Ruler of all Russia, Legend #1), bust R.
(Good coin, price ruble, date, Leg. #2), crowned double eagle.
Many varieties, especially in crown. With or without the Moscow mm. under the eagle. T
rarest varieties of both dates were struck in a collar and are perfectly round.

1643   RUBLE 1707

(Czar Peter Alexievitch, Ruler of all Russia, Leg. #3), bust R.
(Moscow ruble, Leg. #4), crowned double eagle dividing Slavic date below.
Several varieties. With H. G, or no letter on sleeve.

1644   RUBLE 1707

Similar to #1643 with slightly different bust. H on sleeve.
(Moscow ruble, Leg. #4) in two lines divided by crown. Below Slavic date 1707 divided by tai

1645   RUBLE 1707

Similar to #1643.
Similar to #1643 with date 1707 below eagle.
Several varieties. With H, G, or no letter on sleeve.

1646   RUBLE 1707

Similar to #1643 with smaller, thinner bust and G on sleeve.
Similar to #1645.

1647   RUBLE 1710

(Czar Peter Alexievitch, Ruler of all Russia, Leg. #3), large bust R.
(Russian ruble:1710, Leg. #5), Moscow mintmark under eagle's wings.
With or without H on sleeve.

1648   RUBLE 1710

Similar to #1643.
(Good coin, price ruble 1710, Leg. #6), crowned double eagle.

1649   RUBLE 1710

Similar to #1647, another bust with H on sleeve.
Similar to #1648.

1650   RUBLE 1712

(Czar Peter Alexievitch, Leg. #7), slender bust R.
(Moscow ruble .1.7.1.2, Leg. #8), crowned double eagle.
Several varieties. No periods in date. Smaller head. Open crown.

651 RUBLE 1714

Similar to #1647, another bust in armor R.
Similar to #1650 with date 1714.
Variety with 4 over 3.

1652 RUBLE 1718

(Czar Peter Alexievitch, Autocrat of all Russia, Leg. #9), armored bust R, unbroken legend.,
(New coin, price ruble, Leg. #10), Slavic date 1718, crowned double eagle.
Many varieties. Letters OK, KO, or L under bust. Different heads and armor.
A. N normal instead of reversed in date. B. O over A in MAHETA.

1653 RUBLE 1719

Similar to #1652 with another bust.
Similar to #1652 with Slavic date 1719.
Many varieties similar to #1652. Large and small crowns.

1654   RUBLE 1720

Similar to #1652 with another bust.
Similar to #1652 with Slavic date 1720.
Many varieties similar to #1652. No letters or OK, KO, or K under bust.

1655   RUBLE 1721

Similar to #1652 with another bust.
Similar to #1652 with Slavic date 1721.
Many varieties similar to #1652.

1656   RUBLE 1722

(Peter Alexievitch Emperor and Autocrat of all Russia, Leg. #11), bust R.
(New coin, price ruble, Leg. #10), four crowned Russian P's in the form of a cross with 17 - 22 inside the two side P's.
Many varieties in spelling, leaves in wreath, size of date, star above head, etc.

657   RUBLE 1723

Similar to #1656, another bust in armor with open neck, legend broken at bottom.
Similar to #1656 with 17 - 23.
Many varieties in hair arrangement and laurel leaves. OK under bust.

658   RUBLE 1723

Similar to #1656, bust with high neckband, eagle on breast, Order chain, and OK on sleeve, unbroken legend.
Similar to #1657.
Many varieties. Different spellings. Large, medium, small, or no St. Andrew's cross on breast.

659   RUBLE 1724

(Peter I, Emperor and Autocrat of all Russia, Leg. #12), armored bust R with St. Petersburg mintmark below, unbroken legend.
(New coin, price ruble, Leg. #13), similar to #1656 with 17 - 24 and in the center the star of St. Andrew's Order.
Many varieties. Open and covered neck, with or without OK under bust, different spellings, punctuation, hair ribbons.

R

1660   RUBLE 1724

Similar to #1657.
Similar to #1659 with no star in center.
Many varieties similar to #1659. Moscow mint.

1661   RUBLE 1725

Similar to #1659 with another bust, unbroken legend.
Similar to #1659 with 17 - 25.
Many varieties . Different spellings, devices over the head, with or without necktie, with or without star in center on reverse. St. Petersburg mint.

1662   RUBLE 1725

Similar to #1657 with legend broken at bottom.
Similar to #1660 with date 17 - 25.
Several varieties. With or without OK under bust. Moscow mint.

CATHERINE I   1725-1727

663   RUBLE   1725
(Catherine, Empress and Autocrat of all Russia), bust L, unbroken legend.
(New coin, price ruble 1725), crowned double eagle.
Five varieties. The so-called "Mourning ruble."

664   RUBLE   1725-1726
(Catherine, Empress and Autocrat of all Russia), bust L with broken legend.
Similar to #1663.
Many varieties. Moscow and St. Petersburg mints, without mintmark or with mintmark on either side. Moscow mint have lettered edge.

665   RUBLE   1726-1727
Similar to #1664 with new bust R.
Similar to #1664.
Many varieties. Moscow mint with lettered edge. St. Petersburg mint with braided edge.

1666   RUBLE   1727
Similar to #1665.
Similar to #1665, eagle with "crow's" tail.
Two varieties.

PETER II   1727-1730

1667   RUBLE   1727
(Peter II, Emperor and Autocrat of all Russia), bust R.
(New coin, price ruble), four crowned Russian P's in cross form with two I's in angles. 17 - 2
inside the two side P's.
Many varieties. Moscow mint with lettered edge; St. Petersburg mint with braided edge ar
some with mintmark under bust.

1668   RUBLE   1728
Similar to #1667 with another bust.
Similar to #1667 with date 17 - 28.
Many varieties. Moscow mint only.

1669   RUBLE 1729

Similar to #1667 with another bust.
Similar to #1667 with date 17 - 29.
Many varieties. Moscow mint only.

ANNA   1730-1740

1670   RUBLE 1730-1733

(By the grace of God, Anna, Empress and Autocrat of all Russia), bust R.
(Coin ruble date), crowned double eagle with arms on breast.
Many varieties with bust changes, punctuation and spacing differences.

1671   RUBLE 1733-1734

Similar to #1670 with older, narrower bust.
Similar to #1670.
Several varieties of each date.

1672   RUBLE 1734

Similar to #1670 with larger bust, legend broken slightly at top.
Similar to #1670.
Many varieties. A. Date divided by crown.

1673   RUBLE 1734-1737

Similar to #1670 with another bust.
Similar to #1670.
Many varieties.

1674   RUBLE 1736-1740

Similar to #1670, bust with much smaller neater head.
Similar to #1670 with date over eagle.
Many varieties. Hedlinger type.

1675 RUBLE 1738-1740
Similar to #1674 with another bust.
Similar to #1674.
Many varieties. With or without St. Petersburg mintmark. A. With brooch on breast.

IVAN III   1740-1741

1676 RUBLE 1741
(Ioann III by the grace of God, Emperor and Autocrat of all Russia), bust R with St. Petersburg or Moscow
(3 var.) mintmark below.
(Coin ruble 1741), crowned double eagle.

ELISABETH   1741-1762

1677 RUBLE 1741-1754
(By the grace of God, Elisabeth, Empress and Autocrat of all Russia), bust R with St. Petersburg mintmark below.
(Coin ruble date), crowned double eagle with arms on breast.
Many varieties. Usually with a mantle under bust. Those without are rare.

1678   RUBLE 1742-1758

Similar to #1677 without mantle under bust and Moscow mintmark.
Similar to #1677.
Many varieties.

1679   RUBLE 1754-1757

Similar to #1677 with smaller, daintier bust.
Similar to #1677.
St. Petersburg mint. Several varieties of each date.

1680   RUBLE 1757

Similar to #1677 with much larger bust.
Similar to #1677.
St. Petersburg mint. With or without letters by eagle's tail. This is possibly only a pattern.

1681   RUBLE 1757-1761

Similar to #1679 with changed larger bust.
Similar to #1677.
St. Petersburg mint. Several varieties of each date. A. 1761 with a long lock of hair.

PETER III   1762

1682   RUBLE 1762

(Peter III, by the grace of God, Emperor of all Russia), bust R with mintmark below.
(Coin ruble 1762), crowned double eagle with arms on breast.
St. Petersburg or Moscow mint. Several varieties of each mint.

CATHERINE II   1762-1796

1683   RUBLE 1762-1766

(By the grace of God, Catherine II, Empress and Autocrat of all Russia), bust with ruffle
around neck R. Mintmark below.
(Coin ruble date), crowned double eagle with arms on breast.
Several varieties of each date from each mint. No 1766 from St. Petersburg.

1684   RUBLE 1766-1776

Similar to #1683, bust with no ruffle around neck.
Similar to #1683.
St. Petersburg 1766-1776 ; Moscow 1767-1770, 1775. Many varieties. A. 1766-1768 with larger bust.

1685   RUBLE 1777-1785

Similar to #1683, older bust with two long locks of hair.
Similar to #1683.
St. Petersburg mint. Many varieties. A. A 1777 with no letters under eagle.

1686   RUBLE 1785-1796

Similar to #1685 with older, larger bust.
Similar to #1683.
St. Petersburg mint. Larger diameter. A number of varieties. A. A 1793 without letters by eagle.

PAUL I   1796-1801

1687   RUBLE 1796
(Not unto us, not unto us, but unto Thy name) in ornamented square tablet.
(Of year 1796), crowned double eagle with arms on breast. Initials below.
Two varieties.

1688 [278]   RUBLE 1797-1800
Similar to #1687 with initials in bottom corners of the tablet.
(Coin price ruble date), four Russian P's in cross form with I in center.
Several varieties of each date, 4 of 1797, 4 of 1798, 4 of 1799, and 2 of 1800. The 1797 is considerably larger in diameter than the later dates.

LIVONIA

IN 1756 the Czarina Elisabeth of Russia joined an all-European coalition opposing Frederick the Great of Prussia, and moved troops into the Baltic provinces, whose educated and ruling classes were largely German. In an effort to displace the foreign coins circulating there, she ordered special coins struck for Livonia and Estonia under the name of livonaises.

1690   LIVONAISE OF 96 KOPECKS 1757
ELISABETHA. I. D.G. IMP. TOT. ROSS.*., bust R.
MONETA. LIVOESTHONICA. 1757, crowned double eagle with arms of Riga and Revel on breast. 96 below.
Moscow mint. The 1756 is a pattern.

LEGENDS ON RUBLES OF PETER THE GREAT

1. ЦРЬ ПЕТРЪ АЛЕЗІЕВИЧЬ ВСЕА РОСІИ ПОВЕЛИТЕЬ

2. МАНЕТА ДОБРАА ЦЕНА РУБЛЬ

3. ЦРЬ ПЕТРЪ АЛЕЗІЕВИЧЬ В:Р:П.

4. МОСКОВСКИИ РУБЛЬ

5. РОСІИСКОІ РУБЛОВИКЪ : 1710

6. МАНЕТА ДОБРАА ЦЕНА РУБЛЬ

7. ЦРЬ ПЕТРЪ АЛЕЗІЕВИЧЬ

8. МОСКОВСКІ РУБЛЬ 1.7.1.2

9. ЦРЬ ПЕТРЪ АЛЕЗІЕВИЧЬ ВСЕА РОСІИ САМОДЕРЖЕЦЪ

10. МОНЕТА НОВАА ЦЕНА РУБЛЬ

11. ПЕТРЪ А ІМПЕРАТОРЪ І САМОДЕРЖЕЦЪ ВСЕРОССИІСКИИ

12. ПЕТРЪ І ИМПЕРАТОРЪ І САМОДЕРЖЕЦЪ ВСЕРОССІИСКИИ

13. МОНЕТА НОВАЯ ЦЕНА РУБЛЬ

МД - ММД - MOSCOW MINT

СПБ - СП - СМ - БМ - ST. PETERSBURG MINT

1704 - ҂АΨД	1709 - ҂АΨѲ	1714 - ҂АΨДІ	1719 - ҂АΨѲІ
1705 - ҂АΨЕ	1710 - ҂АΨІ	1715 - ҂АΨЕІ	1720 - ҂АΨК
1706 - ҂АΨЅ	1711 - ҂АΨАІ	1716 - ҂АΨЅІ	1721 - ҂АΨКА
1707 - ҂АΨЗ	1712 - ҂АΨВІ	1717 - ҂АΨЗІ	1722 - ҂АΨКВ
1708 - ҂АΨИ	1713 - ҂АΨГІ	1718 - ҂АΨИІ	1723 - ҂АΨКГ

SPAIN

PAIN'S modern history begins in 1469 with the marriage of Isabella of Castile and Leon to her cousin Ferdinand of Aragon. Isabella inherited her throne from her other in 1474 and Ferdinand his from his father in 1479. When the joint sovereigns 1492 subjugated Granada, the last Mohammedan state in the peninsula, and Ferdinand acquired Roussillon in 1493 from France and captured Spanish Navarre in 1512 om his half-sister's family, Spain was territorially intact. Unfortunately the sovergn's only son died, and on Ferdinand's death in 1516 the succession went to his eldest ughter's oldest son. Charles was a Habsburg and succeeded his grandfather Maximilian I as Holy Roman Emperor in 1519. Henceforth for nearly two centuries under eir Habsburg rulers Spain was to be embroiled in European politics from which she enefited not at all and which helped to produce her gradual decline. Charles II, the st of the Habsburgs, died a childless imbecile in 1700, leaving the throne to the duke f Anjou, grandson of Louis XIV of France and of Charles's half sister Maria Theresa.

Louis XIV's decision to allow his seventeen year old grandson to inherit the Spanish rone brought on the War of the Spanish Succession, which was concluded only in 713 by the Peace of Utrecht. Spain lost Gibraltar and Minorca and all possessions in aly and the Netherlands. Philip was obliged to reduce various sections of Spain by rce of arms, and in the process abolished many of the local privileges previously etained. The king's second wife, Elizabeth Farnese of Parma, whom he married in 714, dominated both the king and Spain's foreign policy in an effort to restore panish influence in Italy. She did succeed in providing Italian thrones for two of her ons. Besides Philip's Spanish coinage of 8 reales, which extended from 1701 to 1740, ieces of the same size were issued in his name as duke of Brabant in ducatons and atagons from 1703 to 1709; as count of Flanders, a patagon of 1705; and as duke of lilan, a filippo of 1702 (see these countries).

Philip was succeeded by the second son of his first marriage Ferdinand VI, who eigned from 1746 to 1759.

Ferdinand was followed by his half brother, Charles III (1759-1788). Charles, lizabeth Farnese's oldest son, had been king of Naples and Sicily since 1735, and bdicated that throne in favor of his eight year old younger son Ferdinand in order o become king of Spain. Through his pro-French and anti-English policy he managed o recover some lost Spanish territory during the war of American independence. At ome his policies seem to have been on the whole enlightened and productive of ood for Spain.

Unfortunately, Charles's son, Charles IV (1788-1808), inherited his father's despotism without his enlightenment. He was dull to the point of imbecility and remained most f his life under the influence of his narrow-minded and unfaithful wife, Maria Luisa f Parma.

The French Revolution put an end to the French alliance, but hatred of England ushed Spain into a new alliance with republican France, which lasted until the fall f the Queen's favorite and lover Godoy, Prince of the Peace, in 1798. Napoleon restored lodoy in 1801 and Spain became more than ever a vassal of France. Finally Napoleon lisposed of the Bourbon dynasty entirely and set up his brother Jerome as king of Spain in 1808.

The coat of arms on the obverse of the pieces of Philip V is made up of the arms of Castile and Leon in the upper left quarter, Aragon and Sicily in the upper right, Old and new Burgundy below, Brabant, Tyrol, and Flanders at the bottom, with the Bourbon ilies in the center. The arms for Charles III include at upper left Aragon and Sicily, Old and New Burgundy at right, Parma below at left, Medici at right, and at the bottom Brabant, Tyrol, and Flanders, with Castile and Leon in the center surmounted by the Bourbon lilies. The reverse arms on most of these pieces are those of Castile and Leon.

PHILIP V 1700-1746

1691 **8 REALES 1701**

PHILIPPVS . V.D. - G. HISPANI . REX, crowned shield in Order Chain separating M-S.
PROTECTIONE . 1701. VIRTUTE, cross over monogram MA separating R-8.
Seville mint.

1692 **8 REALES 1704-1707, 1709, 1711**

*PHILIPPVS .V. DEI. GRAT., crowned arms, in field on left .VIII., and on right .S P. or S.M
HISPANIARVM. REX. date, arms in frame.
Seville mint. 1704-1706 with S P. 1707, 1709, 1711 with S.M. 1711 with obverse legen
PHILIPVS * V * D * G * ?

1693 **8 REALES 1706-1707, 1709-1716**

*PHILIPPVS * V * D * G *, crowned arms, in field on left M J, on right .8.
*HISPANIARVM * REX * date, arms in frame.
Madrid mint. The first three dates come on irregular flans. There is a unique specimen of the
1709 on regular flan. The 1711 comes with wide or narrow crown. The 1712, 1714-1716 have
U's for V's and some difference in the rosettes.

94   8 REALES 1707

+ PHILIPPVS. V. DEI. G*, crowned shield with arms of Aragon, in field on left * CA *, on right * 8 *..
* ARAGONVM * REX * 1707 *, shield with arms of Sardinia.
Zaragoza mint.

95   8 REALES 1709

PHILIP. V. D. G.-HISP. ET IND. REX, head R, 1709 below.
DEXTERA. DOMINI. EXALTAVIT. ME *M* *J*, crowned arms.
Madrid mint (M).

96   8 REALES 1718

*PHILIPPVS * V * DEI * GRAT, crowned arms, in field R-8 above and S-M below.
*HISPANIARVM * REX * 1718, arms in frame.
Seville mint (S M).

1697   8 REALES   1726-1735, 1740

* PHILIPPUS * V * D * G *, crowned arms, in field R-8 above, mint initials below.
* HISPANIARUM * REX * date, arms in frame.

Madrid mint 1726, 1729 M and JJ ; 1730-1732, 1734. 1740 M and JF; 1731 M and F. Seville
mint 1728-1729 S and P ; 1731-1735 S and PA; 1735 S and AP. Segovia mint 1727-1729
aqueduct and F.

1698   8 REALES   1729-1730

Similar to #1697 with nothing in field.
Similar to #1697 with * S * date * S *.
Seville mint (S).

CHARLES III   1759-1788

1699   8 REALES   1762

* CAROLUS * III * D * G *, crowned arms, in field R - 8 above, mint initials below.
Similar to #1697.
Madrid mint M and JP. Seville mint S and JV.

OO   8 REALES 1772-1779, 1782 1788

. CAROLUS - III. DEI. G. date., bust R.

HISPANIARUM. REX., crowned arms, in field R - 8 above, mint initials below.

Madrid mint 1772-1774 M and PJ; 1774 M; 1782, 1788 M and M. Seville mint 1772-1779 S and
   CF; 1788 S and C.

CHARLES IV   1788-1808

01 [307]   8 REALES 1788-1793, 1795-1800

. CAROLUS - IIII. DEI. G. date., bust R.

Similar to #1709.

Madrid mint 1789, 1796-1798 M and MF. Seville mint 1788-1792 S and C; 1792-1793, 1795-1800
   S and CN.

SPANISH NETHERLANDS

BY THE Peace of Arras in 1579 the seven northern provinces of the Netherla
established a union and independence. The southern provinces, consisting of
duchies of Brabant, Limburg, and Luxemburg, the counties of Artois, Fland
Hainaut, Namur, and Upper Gelderland, most of which had fallen into the possess
of Burgundy at one time or another, in 1477 were inherited by the Austrian Habsbu
By the division of the Habsburg holdings in 1522 they came under the control of
king of Spain and were subsequently known as the Spanish Netherlands. The Habsb
line in Spain died out with Charles II in 1700, and the French Bourbons succeec
bringing on the War of the Spanish Succession. For a time in the early 18th cent
France controlled the provinces, parts of which she had previously appropriated,
by the Treaty of Utrecht in 1713 they passed officially again to the Austrian Ha
burgs, having been under virtual control of Austria since 1707, and were then kno
as the Austrian Netherlands (which see).

PHILIP V OF SPAIN   1700-c. 1707

1702   DUCATONE OF 2 PESOS 1703, 1705

1703   DUCATONE 1703-1704
PHILIPPUS V.D.G. HISPANIARUM ET INDIARUM REX, bust R with hand (Antwerp) bel
ARCHID. AVST. - DVX. BVRG. - BRABAN. Z c divided date, crowned and supported arms

1704   DUCATONE 1703
Similar to #1703 with low square neck, hand (Antwerp) below.
Similar to #1703.

705   DUCATONE OF 3 PESOS   1703

706   DUCATONE OF 2 PESOS   1703-1705

A. Variety of 1703 with spelling BRABANT

707   DUCATONE   1703-1705

Similar to #1703.
BURGUND - .DUX. - BRABAN. Z c, divided date., crowned and supported arms.

708   PATAGON OF 2 PESOS   1705

709   PATAGON   1703-1706

PHILIPPUS V. D.G. HISPANIARUM ET INDIARUM REX hand (Antwerp), crown over floriated cross, crowned P V's at sides.
BURGUND. DUX - BRABANT. Z c, divided date, crowned arms in double chain.

1710   PATAGON 1705

Similar to #1709 with lily (Bruges) at top.
BURGUND. DUX - C. FLAND. Z c, 17 - 05, crowned arms in double chain.

1711   PATAGON 1709

Similar to #1709 with lion (Namur) at top.
Similar to #1709 with date 17 - 09.

SWEDEN

SWEDEN emerged in 1523 from the Union of Kalmar (formed in 1397 with Denmark and Norway) as an independent nation under a native king, Gustavus Vasa (1523-560), the founder of the modern kingdom. A century later his grandson, Gustavus II Adolphus, enhanced Sweden's prestige by his brilliant leadership in the religious and political wars in the Germanies. Years of continual struggle with most of the northern European states followed the king's death at the battle of Lutzen in 1632. In 1697 his great nephew Charles XI (1660-1697) died, leaving the realm to his fifteen year old son Charles XII, a gifted, precocious, but obstinate youth. A short lived regency was established. In 1700 war with Poland, Denmark, and Russia broke out. After some years of success, especially in Poland and Saxony, the Swedish army was defeated at Poltava in 1709, and Charles fled, a fugitive, to Turkey, where he remained, part of the time as a prisoner, until 1714. In the meantime Sweden had lost most of her Baltic possessions. When the king was shot and killed in 1718, Swedish supremacy in the Baltic was over. The king's favorite minister Baron von Gortz, whose activities among some accomplishments included lowering the value of the currency, was subsequently tried and executed.

Charles's sister, Ulrika Eleonora (1718-1720) was declared not to be his successor but was elected to the throne by a Riksdag determined to rule the nation itself.

In 1720 she was supplanted by her husband, the hereditary Prince Frederick of Hesse, who became Frederick I (1720-1751). Financial troubles embarrassed the administration. Trade and manufacturing were encouraged. But eventually in 1741 war was declared on Russia in the hope of regaining some of the lost prestige. The last years of the reign were plagued by the question of a successor to the throne of the childless couple. The Empress Elizabeth of Russia advocated the candidacy of Duke Adolphus Frederick of Holstein. Russian influence at last prevailed and the duke was elected. He came to Sweden in 1744, and though he married Louisa Ulrika, a sister of the Prussian King, Russian influence remained paramount.

Adolphus Frederick (1751-1771) succeeded in 1751 and almost immediately came into conflict with the noble bureaucracy dominating the Riksdag. Under French influence now, war with Prussia started in 1757. The country was in bad financial straits. Corruption was widespread as foreign powers attempted to buy parliamentary support for their policies. Over the protests of his parents the crown prince married a Danish princess. Battling between the two political parties, the "Hats" and the "Caps," continued to weaken Swedish authority right up to the time of the king's death in 1771.

Gustavus III (1771-1792) returned from Paris on his father's death and within a year had arrested the Council of State and replaced parliamentary government by his own authority. Though able and sincere, the king, through his reforms and desire for personal rule, found himself perpetually in difficulties at home and abroad. War with Russia came in 1788. Though this added prestige and power to the king at home, it ended abroad in a virtual stalemate in 1790 with Swedish finances in a ruinous condition.

The king's death in 1792 brought his thirteen year old son Gustavus IV Adolphus (1792-1809) to the throne. A regency under the king's uncle ruled until the young man came of age in 1796. He had few abilities and his obstinate, passionate nature eventually led to his overthrow in 1809. He died in exile in 1837.

CHARLES XII   1697-1718

1712   8 MARKS 1700, 1701, 1704
CAROLVS. XII. - D. G. REX. SVE.*, bust R.
DOMINVS. PROTECTOR. MEVS. date *, crowned arms separating 8 - M and H - Z.

1713   RIKSDALER 1707
CAROLVS. XII. D.G. - REX. SVECIAE., bust L.
MED. GUDZ. HIELP., crowned and supported arms, below L. 1707. C.

1714   RIKSDALER 1707
CAROLVS. XII. - D.G. REX. SVEC. ETC., short haired bust R.
Similar to #1713.

715   RIKSDALER 1713
CAROLVS. XII - D.G. REX. SVE., bust R.
Similar to #1713 with L. 1713. C. below.

716   RIKSDALER 1718
CAROLVS XII. - D.G. REX SVECIAE, bust R.
Similar to #1713, supporting lions look backwards. L. - C. and 1718 below.

1717   4 CAROLINER 1718
*DOMINVS * PROTECTOR * MEVS*, crowned C's in monogram separating X - 11; 1718 and
L.C. below.
FYRA - CARO - LI - NER, four crowned shields in cross form with 2 D S M crowned in angles.

ULRIKA ELEONORA 1718-1720

1718 RIKSDALER 1719
VLRICA. ELEONORA. - D.G. REGINA. SVEC., bust R.
GUD. MITT. HOPP, crowned and supported arms with L. - C. and 1719 below.

FREDERICK I 1720-1751

1719 RIKSDALER 1721
FRIDERICVS. - D.G. REX. SVECIAE., bust R with AN. IVBIL. 1721. below.
Two facing busts of Gustavus I and Gustavus Adolphus in medallions with names above sur
rounded by palm sprays. In exergue IN. MEMOR. VINDICATAE LIBERT. AC RELIG.
Two varieties in the harness on the king.
To commemorate the second centennial of the introduction of the Reformation into Sweden.

1720 RIKSDALER 1723-1728
FRIDERICUS [.] - D. G. REX [.] SVECIAE [.]. bust R.
GUD MITT HOPP., crowned and supported arms. Date in cartouche below.
Four different busts. There is a 2 Riksdaler of 1723.

721   2 RIKSDALER 1727

722   RIKSDALER 1727

FRIDERIC. ET ULR. ELEON. D. G. REX ET REG. SVEC., accolated busts of the king and queen R.
GUD WART HOPP., otherwise similar to #1720.

723   RIKSDALER 1730-1733

Similar to #1720.
Similar to #1720, initials G-Z added at sides of date.
Six different busts. Varieties of 1731, 1732, 1733 with spelling FREDERICVS. Varieties of 1731, 1732 with spelling SVECIAE not the ligature AE as on #1720.

1724   RIKSDALER 1731

FRIDERICVS. ET. VLR. ELEON. D. G. REX. ET. REG. SVECIAE., accolated busts of king and queen R.
GUD WART HOPP., crowned and supported arms with G.Z. and 1731 in cartouche below.

1725   RIKSDALER   1731
Similar to #1724.
SPLENDET. IN. ORBE. DECVS *, three crowns in center.

1726   RIKSDALER   1731
Similar to #1720.
Inscription in 11 lines, REGI SVO / AVGVSTISSIMO / ITER IN HASSIAM / MENSE IVN.
A. MDCCXXXI / APPARANTI / FELICEM FAVSTAMQVE / ET / PROFECTIONEM /
ET REDITIONEM / A DEO CVNCTA SVECIA / SVPPLICITER / PRECATVR.

1727   RIKSDALER   1734-1738
FRIDERICVS. - D. G. REX. SVECIAE., bust R.
Similar to #1723 with new substructure for arms and G.Z. below date.

1728   RIKSDALER   1738-1744, 1746-1748
Similar to #1727 with unbroken legend.
Similar to #1727 with H.M. below date.
Six different busts. The 1746-1748 have FRIDERICUS.

1729   RIKSDALER   1748
Similar to #1728 the 1748 date.
GUD MITT HOPP., crowned arms of Sweden only in Order chain separating 17 - 48. Below
D. 17 - APR. and H. - M.

1730   RIKSDALER   1750-1751
Similar to #1729.
GUD MITT HOPP., crowned combined arms in Order chain separating date. Below H. - M.

ADOLPHUS FREDERICK   1751-1771

1731   RIKSDALER 1751-1757. 1759-1766
ADOLPHUS. FRID. D. G. REX SVECIAE., head R.
SALUS. PUBLICA.-SALUS. MEA. date °, crowned arms in Order chain.
Three different heads. No period after ADOLPHUS on some.
1751-1762 have H.M. on reverse ; 1763-1766 have A.L.

1732   RIKSDALER 1767-1769
ADOLPHUS. FRID. D. G. REX. SVECIAE., head R.
SALUS. PUBLICA - SALUS. MEA. date, crowned arms in Order chain separating I. - Rd. with
    A. - L. below.
The 1767 has larger crowns in the arms.

1733   RIKSDALER 1770-1771
Similar to #1732.
SALUS. PUBLICA. SALUS. MEA., crowned arms in chain separating 3. - D., S. - M., A. - L.,
    and parts of date.

GUSTAVUS III   1771-1792

734   RIKSDALER 1771-1775
GUSTAVUS III. D. G. REX SVECIAE., head R.
FADERNESLANDET., otherwise similar to #1733.
The 1775 has the head of #1735.
1771-1773 have A.L. on reverse; the 1774-1775 have O.L.

1735   RIKSDALER 1775-1777
Similar to #1734.
Similar to #1734 with I. - Rd. added at sides and O. - L. below.

1736   RIKSDALER 1779-1783, 1787-1788, 1790-1792
Similar to #1734.
Similar to #1735 with 3.D. and S.M. removed.

GUSTAVUS IV ADOLPHUS   1792-1809

1737   RIKSDALER   1792-1795

GUSTAF IV ADOLPH SV. G. OCH W. KONUNG., head R.
GUD   OCH FOLKET., crowned arms in chain separating I. - Rd., O. - L. and date.
The head on each date differs somewhat.

1738   RIKSDALER   1796-1797

Similar to #1737, new head with flowing hair R.
Similar to #1737.

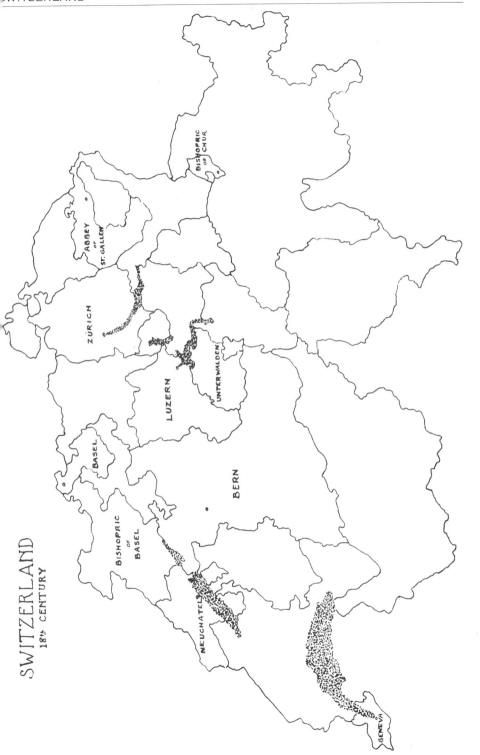

SWITZERLAND
18th CENTURY

BISHOPRIC
OF CHUR

ABBEY
OF
ST. GALLEN

ZÜRICH

UNTERWALDEN

LUZERN

BASEL

BERN

BISHOPRIC
OF
BASEL

NEUCHATEL

GENEVA

SWITZERLAND

SWITZERLAND is a combination of parts of the old Germanic, Burgundian, and Italian kingdoms, based on the three original forest cantons, Uri, Schwyz, and Unterwalden, which formed a union in 1291. Largely Germanic in origin and nature the union slowly obtained independence from the Holy Roman Empire, practically in 1499, officially in 1648. Being a loose federation of cantons, unified mainly for defense purposes, it appeared otherwise hopelessly diverse—socially, linguistically, religiously physically, and politically. By 1400 the Confederation had eight members and after 1513 thirteen, with numerous allied and protected districts.

During the Reformation and Counter-Reformation the Swiss were torn in various ways. Sometimes the divisions were along Catholic-Protestant lines, sometimes along French-Austrian, and sometimes the result of purely local conditions. During the latter half of the seventeenth century the League was under the control of the Catholics, but as a result of French-Austrian-Spanish politics a new war between predominantly religious contenders broke out, and this time the great Protestant city states triumphed and established their position by the Treaty of Aarau 1712.

During the remainder of the eighteenth century until the French Revolution small change occurred politically. During this time, however, wealth, population, agriculture, manufacturing increased enormously. But democratic forms of government developed very slowly. All the thirteen quasi-independent allied cantons and their thirteen associated states were under various forms of autocratic government. These were divided technically into " democratic " cantons—Uri, Schwyz, Unterwalden, Zug, Glarus, Appenzell—ruled by a few families ; Guild cantons—Zürich, Basel, Schaffhausen—rigidly controlled by great craft guilds ; " aristocratic " cantons—Bern, Luzern, Freiburg, Solothurn ; a federal type—Valais ; as monarchial—Neuchâtel, with a prince as ruler ; and ecclesiastical—Bishops of Basel and Chus, Abbots of St. Gallen and Engelberg. The class distinction was definitely that of rulers and ruled.

The French Revolution changed all this. After the French occupation of the country in 1797, Napoleon transformed the old league into the centralized Helvetian Republic, a federation which survived until 1803. A unified currency was issued during these years.

The taler issuing cantons during the eighteenth century included Basel, Bern, Luzern, Unterwalden, and Zürich, long time members of the Confederation; Geneva, the powerful French speaking city and small canton in the southwest, which was to join in 1814; and Neuchatel, also not a regular member until 1814, which was ruled by the kings of Prussia as princes of Neuchatel. Three ecclesiastical states likewise issued large size silver pieces in this century.

BISHOPRIC OF BASEL

THE Bishopric of Basel dates from the 5th century in the city of Basel. By the 14th century the bishops' power was challenged by the burghers, and when the city ccepted the Reformation, the bishops moved their seat in 1525 to Porrentruy, where hey resided until 1792. France annexed much of the territory, but after the Napoleonic ars it was incorporated into Bern.

JOHANN CONRAD VON REINACH-HIRTZBACH   1705-1737

739   TALER 1716

*IOANNES * CONRADVS * D * G *, bust R.
*EPIS * BASILEENSIS * S * R * I * PRINC * 17 - 16, crowned double eagle with arms on breast.

BASEL

740   2 TALERS N.D.

MONETA * NOVA * VRBIS * BASILEENSIS, city arms surrounded by eight shields.
DOMINE * CONSERVA * NOS * IN * PACE, double eagle in border.

1741   2 TALERS   N.D.
BASILEA in ribbon above city view.
Eight shields around. * DOMINE. CONSERVA. NOS. IN. PACE in band around city arms.

1742   2 TALERS   N.D.
* DOMINE. CONSERVA. NOS. IN. PACE. In beaded border BASILEA over city view.
Eight shields around, in center basilisk holding city arms.
A. Variety with changed size of lettering in BASILEA and 6 ships instead of 3.

1743   TALER   N.D.
BASILEA in cartouche over city view.
* DOMINE. CONSERVA. NOS. IN. PACE, basilisk with city arms surrounded by eight shields.
A. Variety with reverse legend in smaller letters.

1744 TALER N.D.

BASILEA in band over city view.
*.DOMINE. CONSERVA. NOS. IN. PACE., two basilisks supporting shield with city arms.
A. Variety with 8 ships instead of 7; B. Variety with * BASILEA * not in a band and changed city view.

1745 TALER N.D.

BASILEA in band over city view.
* DOMINE * CONSERVA * NOS * IN * PACE *, two basilisks supporting shield with city arms, all in border.

1746 TALER N.D.

City view, clouds above.
DOMINE * CONSERVA * NOS * IN * PACE *, city arms in elaborate shield.

1747 TALER N.D.

BASILEA in cartouche over city view. Six ships on the river.
DOMINE. CONSERVA. NOS. IN. PACE *, basilisk with shield of city arms, IDB below.
Four varieties. A. Three ships. B. Five ships. C. Seven ships.

1748 2 TALERS 1740

Eight shields over BASILEA in cartouche, city view, below in exergue 1740 and I.H.
* DOMINE. CONSERVA. NOS. IN. PACE, basilisk holding shield with city arms.
This is probably an essay.

1749 2 TALERS 1741

Similar to #1748 with all details changed and initials HM.
Similar to #1748 with different basilisk and shield.

750   TALER 1741

Similar to #1749 smaller size.
Similar to #1749 smaller size.

751   TALER 1756

BASILEA over city view. In exergue ornamentation dividing 17 - 56. H at right.
* DOMINE CONSERVA NOS IN PACE, basilisk with shield.

752   TALER 1756

Similar to #1751.
DOMINE CONSERVA NOS IN PACE, basilisk with shield on base. H in exergue.

1753   2 TALERS 1762

BASILEA in band supported by cherub, city view, below in cartouche MDCCLXII, and I at bottom.
Similar to #1749 with altered details.
This is probably an essay.

1754   TALER 1765

MONETA REIPUB. BASILEENSIS 1765. In center in wreath I THALER. I - H in bow ribbon.
* DOMINE. CONSERVA. NOS. IN. PACE, basilisk with shield.
A. Variety with much smaller lettering on reverse and ornament below shield.

1755   TALER 1785

Eight shields over city view. In exergue BASILEA 1785 over sprays.
Similar to #1752.

756   TALER   1793

City view. In exergue BASILEA 1793 over sprays.
Similar to #1752.
Two varieties.

757   TALER   1793

Similar to #1756.
Similar to #1756, new arrangement of basilisk and shield.

758   TALER   1795-1796

RESPVBLICA BASILIENSIS. Arms under hat, between sprays, on a standard.
DOMINE / CONSERVA NOS / IN PACE / MDCCXCV or VI in wreath.
The two dates differ in many details. There is no bar over the date on the 1796.

BERN

1759   40 BATZEN   1795-1796

RESPUBLICA BERNENSIS, crowned shield with arms of Bern.
DOMINUS PROVIDEBIT, standing knight with sword, date below.
Many varieties, especially of the 1795, differing in the figure of the knight and the groun
under him. A. Variety of 1795 with a single plume on the hat.

1760   TALER   1798

Similar to #1759 with the shield sunk in an oval panel.
Similar to #1759 with the knight sunk in an oval panel.
Two main varieties. A. Heavy knight with small date. B. Thin knight with large date. Als
two sizes in the bear.

BISHOPRIC OF CHUR

THE bishopric of Chur located in the northern part of the canton of Graubünden dates from the 5th century. The bishops became directly dependent upon the Empire, nd in 1170 were made princes, apparently with coining privileges. Until the Reformaion the bishops were the dominant power in the canton. In 1526, after the city of hur and the surrounding territory had accepted Protestantism, the bishops lost their emporal authority but continued their coinage.

ULRICH VIII VON FEDERSPIEL   1692-1728

761   TALER 1720
VDAL: S.R.I: PR: EP: CVR - D: IN. FIRST B: ET. FvNAW ✷ in border, bust R.
CAROLVS. VI. D:G: ROM: IMP: S:A: 1720 in border, crowned double eagle with shield on breast.

JOSEPH BENEDICT VON ROST   1728-1754

762   2 TALERS 1736

763   TALER 1736
.IOS. BENED. D.G. EPISCOPVS. CVRIENS. S.R.I. PRINCEPS. in beaded border, bust R. In cartouche below H.L.C.
.D. IN. FVRST. ET. FVRSTENAV. EX. L.B. DE. ROST., cardinal's hat over arms, above 17 - 36.

JOHANN ANTON VON FEDERSPIEL   1755-1777

1764   TALER 1766

IOANNES. ANTONIUS. D:G: EP: CUR: S:R:I: PR., capped and mantled arms with mac and sword behind.
D: IN. FURSTENBURG - ET. FURSTENAU*, within a wreath AD / NORMAM / CONVEN* / 1766
A 2 taler piece is also reported

1766   TALER 1766

Similar to #1764.
IOSEPHUS. II: D:G: ROM: IMP: SEMP: AUG: *17 - 66, crowned double eagle with haloes.

GENEVA

1767   TALER 1721-1723

RESPUBLICA - GENEVENSIS(.), rayed sun with IHS above shield.
POST TENEBRAS LUX and date in border, crowned double eagle.
The 1722 has sprays on either side of the date. Two sizes of the crown on the reverse of the 1723

768   TALER 1794

REPUBLIQUE GENEVOISE, turreted head of Liberty, below EGALITE LIBERTE / INDE-
PENDANCE / T.B.
APRES LES TENEBRES LA LUMIERE, in center between wheat heads, PRIX / DU /
TRAVAIL. / L'AN III. DE / L'EGALITE / 1794

769   TALER OF 12 FLORINS 1795

GENEVE. REPUBLIQUE above, below L'AN. IV. DE. L'EGALITE, arms in wreath.
* POST * TENEBRAS * LUX *, T. 1795 B. In center in a rayed sun XII FLORINS IX SOLS.

770   TALER OF 12 FLORINS 1796

Similar to #1769 except L'AN V.
* POST TENEBRAS LUX * above, below XII FLORINS 1796 IX SOLS, in center IHS in a
rayed sun.

HELVETIAN REPUBLIC

1771   40 BATZEN 1798
HELVET: REPUBL:, knight with sword and standard, 1798 below.
40 BATZEN and B (Basel) or S (Solothurn) in wreath.
On B the letters are more widely spaced and the wreath differs slightly.

1772   4 FRANKEN 1799
HELVETISCHE ornament REPUBLIK in border, knight with sword and standard, 1799 below
4 FRANKEN and B (Bern) in wreath.

1773   4 FRANKEN 1799
Similar to #1772.
Similar to #1772 but a completely different wreath.

LUZERN

774 TALER 1714

MONETA / REIPVP. / LVCERNEN: / SIS. in elaborate wreath, 1714 below.
SANCTVS - LEODEGARIVS, seated saint with stars and H.L. below.
Two dies of each side. A. Variety with reverse legend LEODEGARIVS - SANCTVS and nothing below saint.

1775 40 BATZEN 1796

RESPUBLICA - LUCERNENSI., crowned shield in sprays, below 40. BAZ.
DOMINUS SPES POPULI SUI 1796, in center 8 L's interlocked.
There are several dies. A. With LUCERNENS.

NEUCHÂTEL

FRIEDRICH I. KING OF PRUSSIA   1701-1713

1776   TALER 1713
FRID. D.G. REX. BOR. ET. EL. S. PR. AR. NEOC. ET. VAL. &., bust R with I.P. below.
SVVM - CVIQVE., crowned shield, 1713 below.

FRIEDRICH WILHELM I. KING OF PRUSSIA   1713-1740

1777   TALER 1714
FRID. WILH. D.G. REX. BOR. & EL. S. PR. AR. NEOC. & VAL., bust R with L below.
Crowned shield dividing 17 - 14.

ABBEY OF ST. GALLEN

THE Abbey of St. Gallen had its origin in a cell of an Irish hermit built in 614. In the 8th century it became a Benedictine monastery, which in the following centuries vastly increased in power and in reputation as a seat of learning. About 1205 he abbot was made a prince of the Empire. Bitterness between the town burghers and he abbots arose, especially after the former became Protestants. Both town and abbey were admitted to the Swiss Diet as allies. In 1798 the abbey was secularized and in 1805 incorporated into the canton of St. Gallen.

BEDA ANGEHRN OF HAGENWYL   1767-1796

778   TALER 1776, 1777, 1779
BEDA. D. G. - S. R. I. P *, mantled arms over smaller arms in sprays.
ABB. S. G. - E. S. I. A. V. E., bear in wreath, date below.
The three dates differ in almost all details. The 1779 is very rare.·

779   TALER 1780
Similar to #1778 with different arms and arrangement.
Similar to #1778 with legend beginning A. B. B. S. G. etc.

UNTERWALDEN (OBWALDEN)

1780   TALER   1732

MONETA REIPUBL: SUBSYLVANIAE SUPERIORIS., arms in elaborate frame dividing
17 - 32.

B: NICOLAUS DE - FLUE. HELV. CATH: PATR:, saint kneeling to L.

The status of the 1729, 1731, and other 1732 pieces is doubtful.

ZÜRICH

1781   TALER   1707

MONETA NOVA REIPUBLICAE TIGURINAE *, lion holding sword and shield facing L in
beaded border.

DOMINE / CONSERVA / NOS IN / PACE. / 1707. in wreath.

82   TALER 1709

MONETA REIPVBLICAE TIGVRINAE *, lion similar to #1781 with new shield.
Similar to #1781 except for date.

83   TALER 1713-1717

TIGURINAE * MONETA * REIPUBLICAE, lion with sword and new shield.
IUSTITIA / ET / CONCORDIA / date in wreath.

784   TALER 1722-1724, 1726-1728

MONETA REIPUBLICAE TIGURINAE, two lions supporting shield on base.
DOMINE CONSERVA NOS IN PACE above city view. Date in cartouche below, at upper
left HIG.

1785   TALER   1722, 1725

Similar to #1783 with grass under lion.
Similar to #1784.

1786   TALER   1724-1727, 1730, 1732, 1734

Similar to #1783 with various bases under lion.
IUSTITIA / ET / CONCORDIA and date under ornamented frame with sprays below.

1787   TALER   1729-1730, 1732

MONETA REIPUBLICAE TIGURINAE., lion with sword and new shield.
Similar to #1784.

88   TALER 1734, 1736, 1739

Similar to #1787 with larger lion and star over sword.
Similar to #1784 with changes in the churches at left.
A. A 1734 with obverse of #1783.

89   TALER 1736, 1739, 1741, 1743, 1745, 1748, 1751, 1753, 1756, 1758, 1761, 1767-1768

Similar to #1787 or #1788.
DOMINE / CONSERVA / NOS IN / PACE / date in frame and sprays.
The 1736-1751 have a star over the sword and on the reverse a cherub head at the top. The 1753-1768 have no star and no cherub's head.
A. Variety of 1768 with obverse of #1786 and new frame on reverse.

790   TALER 1741, 1743

MONETA REIPUBLICAE TIGURI., two lions supporting shield on base look out.
Similar to #1788.

1791   TALER 1745, 1748, 1751, 1753, 1756, 1758, 1761
Similar to later dates of #1789.
Similar to #1788.
A. A 1758 with 2 ships in outer harbor and 1 in inner.

1792   TALER 1773
MONETA REIPUBLICAE TURICENSIS, lion with sword and shield facing front.
* IUSTITIA ET CONCORDIA * 1773 in border; sword, fruit and flowers on table.
This so-called Gessner taler is almost always found in proof.

1793   TALER 1773
Similar to #1792.
IUSTITIA / ET / CONCORDIA / 1773 in ornate frame.

794   TALER 1776-1777

MONETA REIPUBLICAE TURICENSIS., smaller lion and larger shield.
Similar to #1793, frame with cornucopias at bottom.

795   TALER 1779

Similar to #1794 with hat on top of shield.
IUSTITIA / ET / CONCORDIA / 1779 in thin wreath.
There are two dies of each side.

1796   TALER 1780

Similar to #1794.
Similar to #1795 except for date and new thin wreath.

1797   TALER 1780

MONETA REIPUBLICAE TURICENSIS., two lions supporting shield on base with hat abov
Similar to #1796.

1798   TALER 1783, 1794, 1796

MONETA REIPUBLICAE TURICENSIS., shield with hat and sprays above, crouching lion
at base.
XI / AUF I. FEINE / MARK. / date. in wreath.
The three dates differ in many details, especially in the size of the letters and figures on th
reverse.

1799   TALER 1790

Similar to #1798.
Similar to #1788 with some changes in the view.
There are two obverse dies and two reverse ones (with changed towers at R).

TURKEY

THE Ottoman Turks first appeared in the western world in 1227, finally settled around Brusa, and established an independent kingdom upon the death of Ala-ud-din, the the last of the Seljukian dynasty, from whom they inherited considerable territory in Asia Minor. Gradually they conquered the Greeks, and extended their influence southward and eastward. Expansion continued until they were checked by Tamerlane at the battle of Angora in 1402. Constantinople fell to them in 1453, and the Eastern Empire of the Greeks was replaced by the Ottoman Empire of the Turks.

Expansion continued in Asia Minor, the Balkans, Egypt, and some Mediterranean islands. The treaty of Karlowitz in 1699 signalized the high water mark of Turkey's offensive against the European nations, and brought her into closer contact with European politics. Disorders persisted at home and the sultan Mustafa II was forced to abdicate in 1703 to be succeeded by his brother Ahmad III.

The defeat of Charles XII of Sweden at Poltava in 1709 and his flight to Turkey involved the latter in a new war with Russia to Peter the Great's discomfiture. This success was followed by war against Venice (1715) and Austria (1716) in which Turkey did not fare so well. War in Persia resulted in the loss of Tabriz; the Janissaries revolted in Istambul; and the sultan abdicated in favor of his nephew Mahmud I.

War with Persia broke out anew in 1733 and with Russia again in 1736 and with Austria in 1738. The peace of 1739 was much to Turkey's advantage. New troubles with Persia in 1743 did not finally alter the treaty of ten years earlier.

Osman III succeeded his brother in 1754 for an undistinguished reign of four years. His cousin Mustafa III concluded a treaty of friendship with Prussia in 1761. The aggressive policies of Catherine II of Russia toward Poland and the Black and Caspian sea regions eventually brought on another war in 1768. Mustafa died in 1773 after repeated Turkish setbacks. His brother Abdul Hamid I made a humiliating peace much to Russia's aggrandizement. The Crimea and the northern Black sea region were declared independent. Catherine wanted these territories, and in 1784 Turkey was forced to accept Russian sovereignty there. War with Russia and Austria flared again in 1788 and in the following year the sultan died.

His nephew and successor Selim III was forced to sign another compromising treaty in 1792. Peace gave the sultan an opportunity to promulgate many reforms which he pushed thru against much opposition. The growing friendship with France was rudely shattered by Napoleon's occupation of Egypt, and Turkey joined Russia and England in a coalition against France. Peace came again only in 1802.

As the standard of the currency was continually reduced during the century, an approximate weight for each type in each reign has been added. The nomenclature is also confused. The following may help to identify some similar pieces.

2½ Piastres=100 paras=Yuzluk

2 Piastres=80 paras=Ikilik

2 Zolota=60 paras=Altmishlik

Piastre=40 paras=Ghurush

Zolota=30 paras

MUSTAFA II   1695-1703   (1106-1115)

1800   PIASTRE   1106
Four line inscription [Sultan of the two lands and Khaqan of the two seas, Sultan, son of
Sultan]
Four line inscription [Sultan Mustafa, son of Muhammad Khan, may his kingdom continue
struck at Constantinople, 1106]
Weight c. 310 grains.

1801   PIASTRE   1106
Similar to #1800.
Similar to #1800 but Adrianople mint.
Weight c. 310 gr.

1802   PIASTRE   1106
Similar to #1800.
Similar to #1800 but Smyrna mint.
A. Another variety struck at the Erzerum mint.
Weight c. 310 gr.

803 PIASTRE 1106

Overstrikes on various European pieces and other Turkish piastres.
Rev. Tughra [May his kingdom continue, struck at Constantinople, 1106]
Weight 300-400 gr.

AHMAD III 1703-1730 (1115-1143)

1804 PIASTRE 1115

Similar to #1800.
Tughra [Struck at Constantinople, 1115]
Weight c. 415 gr.

³05 ZOLOTA 1115

Similar to #1800.
Four line inscription [Sultan Ahmad, son of Muhammad Khan, may his kingdom continue,
struck at Constantinople, 1115]
Weight c. 300 gr.

MAHMUD I   1730-1754   (1143-1168)

1806   PIASTRE   1143
Similar to #1800.
Tughra [Struck at Constantinople, 1143]
Three general types. A. Wide beaded border. B. Rope border. C. No border.
Weight c. 370 gr.

1807   ZOLOTA   1143
Similar to #1806.
Similar to #1806.
Weight c. 290 gr.

OSMAN III   1754-1757   (1168-1171)

1808   PIASTRE   1168
Similar to #1800.
Tughra [Struck at Constantinople,˙ 1168]
Weight c. 365 gr.

MUSTAFA III 1757-1773 (1171-1187)

1809 2 ZOLOTA 1171 (1178, 1179, 1181)
Similar to #1800 with regnal year added.
Four line inscription [Sultan Mustafa, son of Ahmad Khan, may his kingdom continue, struck
 at Islambul, 1171]
A. Variety with much smaller date.
Weight c. 445 gr.

1810 PIASTRE 1171 (1177)
Tughra in wide beaded border.
Regnal year, Islambul mint, date 1171.
Weight c. 300 gr.

1811 PIASTRE 1171 (1173-1176, 1182-1185)
Tughra in narrow border.
Similar to #1810.
Weight c. 300 gr.

1812   ZOLOTA   1171   (1185-1187)
Similar to #1809 with smaller flan.
Similar to #1809 with smaller flan.
Weight c. 225 gr.

ABDUL HAMID I   1773-1789   (1187-1203)

1813   2 PIASTRES   1187   (1202)
Tughra
Regnal year, Constantinople mint, date 1187.
Weight c. 600 gr.

1814   2 ZOLOTA   1187   (REGNAL YEAR ,3, 7, 8, 9, 11, 12, 14)
Similar to #1809.
Four line inscription [Sultan Abdul Hamid, son of Ahmad Khan, may his kingdom continue, struck at Constantinople, 1187]
Weight c. 425 gr.

815 PIASTRE 1187 (REGNAL YEAR 1, 3, 4, 6, 8, 9, 10, 12, 14, 15)
Similar to #1809.
Tughra, Constantinople mint, date 1187.
A. Variety with flower at upper R on reverse like #1807.
Weight 250-300 gr.

1816 ZOLOTA 1187
Similar to #1814 with smaller flan.
Similar to #1814 with smaller flan.
Weight c. 225 gr.

SELIM III   1789-1807   (1203-1222)

1817 [396]   YUZLUK 1203 (REGNAL YEARS 1-6, 8-10)
Similar to #1809 with box around two lines and side ornaments.
Tughra [Struck at Islambul, 1203]
Weight c. 500 gr.

1818 [397] 2 PIASTRES 1203 (REGNAL YEARS 1-4, 6-8, 11)
Tughra
Regnal year, Islambul mint, date 1203.
Weight c. 400 gr.

1819   2 ZOLOTA 1203 (REGNAL YEARS 1-3, 6, 10, 12)
Similar to #1809.
Four line inscription [Sultan Selim, son of Mustafa Khan, may his kingdom continue, struck at Islambul, 1203]
Weight c. 300 gr.

CRIMEA

1820   PIASTRE 1191 [1777] (REGNAL YEARS 2, 4-6)
Tughra
[Struck at Baghchih Serai, 1191]
Weight c. 320 gr.

UNITED NETHERLANDS

THE history of what we know today as Holland or the Netherlands began with the Union of Utrecht 1579, which joined the provinces of Gelders, Holland, Utrecht, nd Zeeland with the county of Zutphen, and which declared independence from the Spanish king Philip II (for earlier history see the Spanish Netherlands). For seventy ears intermittent warfare with Spain and the southern provinces flared, during which he Dutch, at first under the leadership of William the Silent of the House of Orange-Nassau until his murder in 1584, gradually pushed their hegemony southward. The Peace of Munster 1648 formally acknowledged the independence of the United Provinces. The Republic was by no means united, parts recognizing the authority of members of the House of Orange as stadholders, other provinces insisting on a decentralized states government. Wars with France and England, with the loss of the Dutch colony of New Amsterdam in America to the English in 1664 as one of the incidents, occupied much of the second half of the century.

The picture was partially changed by the revolution of 1688 in England, which brought to the English throne William III, Prince of Orange, who had married the Princess Mary, daughter of James II of England. He died childless in 1702, and a collateral branch of the family began the slow and laborious task of acquiring an ascendency over all the Dutch provinces, beginning with Groningen and Friesland, the two always faithful to the House. It was not until 1747 that all seven provinces were finally under control of the stadholder and the Estates General.

The decline in power and world influence of the United Netherlands in the eighteenth century is fairly steady. After some distinguished forebearers the stadholders of the House of Orange in this century were not forceful leaders, and the country suffered a humiliating peace with England in 1785 after the American Revolution. Internal collapse followed; the Prussians invaded in 1787, the French in 1794, and in 1795 the old order was abolished and the Batavian Republic established. The coins issued subsequent to 1795, while similar to the earlier issues, are officially pieces of the Republic.

Rather surprisingly in the midst of a century of disasters the monetary system, revised in 1690, remained relatively stable. With the gulden as the basic unit, ducatons or silver riders and silver ducats, both of which had originated in 1659, and 3 gulden pieces commencing in 1680 were coined by most of the provinces with some regularity throughout the century. The old lion daalder lingered on briefly. The 100 stivers pieces were siege coins issued in Maastricht while it was besieged for seven weeks in the fall of 1794 by a French army under General Kléber and defended by an Austrian garrison of 9,000 men under the Prince of Hesse.

1821   LION DAALDER 1701 (OVERIJSSEL)
MON. ARG CONF - BEL PRO. TRANS, knight with shield.
CONFIDENS. DNO. NON. MOVETVR17 - 01, lion in border.

1822   LION DAALDER 1713 (WEST FRIESLAND)
MO. ARG. PRO: CON. - FOE. BELG. WEST. F., knight with shield.
CONFIDENS. DNO. NON. MOVETVR. 1713, lion in border.

1823   2 DUCATON (SILVER RIDER) 1716 (GELDERS)

**1824   DUCATON (SILVER RIDER) 1704, 1711, 1717, 1720-1721, 1723, 1730,
1733-1738, 1759-1761, 1764-1767, 1773-1775, 1785, 1789-1792
(GELDERS)**
MO. NO: ARG: PRO: CONF - BELG: D: GEL: &: C:Z:; rider on horseback, Gelders arms
below.
CONCORDIA - RES PARVAE - CRESCUNT., crowned and supported arms with date in cartouche below.

1825   3 DUCATON (SILVER RIDER) 1754 (HOLLAND)

1826   2 DUCATON (SILVER RIDER) 1719, 1721, 1745, 1754 (HOLLAND)

**1827   DUCATON (SILVER RIDER) 1741-1744, 1746, 1748, 1750, 1754, 1756-
1762, 1765-1767, 1770-1775, 1779-1780, 1784, 1788-1793 (HOLLAND)**
MO: NO: ARG: CON - FOE: BELG: PRO: HOL: shield, rider on horseback, Holland arms
below.
Similar to #1824.

28   2 DUCATON (SILVER RIDER) 1718 (OVERIJSSEL)

29   DUCATON (SILVER RIDER) 1720, 1732-1738, 1764 (OVERIJSSEL)
MO:NO: ARG: CONFOE-BELG: PRO: TRANSI, bird, rider on horseback, Overijssel arms below.
Similar to #1824.

30   DUCATON (SILVER RIDER) 1736, 1738-1742, 1744, 1746-1747 (OVERIJSSEL)
MO. NO, ARG. CONFOE. BELG. PRO. TRANSISALANIA., rider on horseback, Overijssel arms below but unbroken legend.
Similar to #1824.

331   2 DUCATON (SILVER RIDER) 1715, 1730-1732, 1735, 1740, 1772, 1774-1776 (UTRECHT)

332   DUCATON (SILVER RIDER) 1709-1712, 1718, 1720, 1723, 1726, 1727, 1730-1733, 1735, 1736, 1738-1776, 1778-1782, 1784-1794, 1796, 1798 (UTRECHT)
Similar to #1827 with legend ending TRAI., rider with Utrecht arms below.
Similar to #1824.

1833   2 DUCATON (SILVER RIDER)   1707 (WEST FRIESLAND)

1834   DUCATON (SILVER RIDER)   1713, 1716, 1722, 1727, 1730-1732, 17:
         1742, 1747, 1749, 1752, 1755, 1758-1762, 1765-1768, 1770-1775, 17
         1780, 1782-1786, 1789-1793 (WEST FRIESLAND)
         MO: NO: ARG: CONFOE - BELG: PRO: WESTF:, rider, West Friesland arms below.
         Similar to #1824.

1835   2 DUCATON (SILVER RIDER) 1741, 1747, 1748, 1754 (ZEELAND)

1836   DUCATON (SILVER RIDER)   1716-1717, 1735, 1741-1742, 1744, 1746,
         1750-1762, 1766-1767, 1769, 1771-1776, 1785, 1789-1794 (ZEELAND)
         MO(N): NO(V): ARG: PRO: CON - FOE (D): BELG: COM: ZE(E)L., rider, Zeelan
         arms below.
         Similar to #1824.

1837   SILVER DUCAT 1707-1711, 1734, 1739 (GELDERS)
         MO: ARG: PRO: CON - FOE. BELG. D: GEL. C.Z., standing knight with Gelders ar
         Legend broken below knight.
         CONCORDIA: RES: PARVAE: CRESCUNT, stork, crowned arms separating date.

138 [227]   SILVER DUCAT 1745, 1750, 1753-1755, 1759-1768, 1771, 1773-1775, 1785, 1795, 1797. 1800 (GELDERS)

MO: ARG: PRO: CONF: BELG: D: GEL: &: C: Z:, standing knight with Gelders arms, unbroken legend.
Similar to #1837.

139   2 SILVER DUCATS 1734-1735 (HOLLAND)

140 [226]   SILVER DUCAT 1735, 1751-1753, 1755, 1762-1763, 1767, 1771-1772, 1796-1800 (HOLLAND)

MO: NO: ARG: PRO: CONFOE: BELG: (CO:) HOL(L):, standing knight with Holland arms.
Similar to #1838, except for punctuation.

141   SILVER DUCAT 1701, 1707-1709, 1795-1796 (OVERIJSSEL)

MO: NO: ARG: CONFOE: BELG: PRO: TRANSI:, standing knight with Overijssel arms, unbroken legend.
Similar to #1838.

1842   SILVER DUCAT 1734-1747, 1764, 1767 (OVERIJSSEL)
MO: NO: ARG: CONFOE - BELG: PRO: TRANSI, standing knight with Overijssel arm
broken legend.
Similar to #1837 with : and stork * at legend end.

1843   SILVER DUCAT 1711, 1721, 1727 (UTRECHT)
MO. NO. ARG. PRO. CON - FOE BELG. TRAI _ arms, standing knight with Utrecht ar
separating date.   ,
Similar to #1837 without date.

1844   2 SILVER DUCATS 1772, 1774, 1776 (UTRECHT)

1845 [225]   SILVER DUCAT 1735, 1738-1739, 1746-1749, 1751-1753, 175
1758, 1760-1769, 1771-1776, 1779-1781, 1783,-1792, 1794-1800
(UTRECHT)
Similar to #1840 with legend ending TRAI., knight with Utrecht arms.
Similar to #1838.

846 **SILVER DUCAT 1707-1708, 1746-1747, 1752, 1754, 1756-1757, 1759, 1761, 1763-1765, 1767, 1770-1776, 1781, 1784-1785, 1787, 1789-1796 (WEST FRIESLAND)**

Similar to #1840 with legend ending WESTFRI:, knight with West Friesland arms.
Similar to #1840 but no legend above crown.

847 **2 SILVER DUCATS 1747-1748, 1777 (ZEELAND)**

848 **SILVER DUCAT 1701, 1703-1708, 1713-1721, 1727, 1735, 1737-1738, 1747-1748, 1750, 1757-1782, 1784-1796, 1798 (ZEELAND)**

MO(N). NO(V). ARG. PRO. CONFOE(D). BELG. COM. ZE(E)L., knight with Zeeland arms.
Similar to #1840.
Variety of 1757 with beaded borders on both sides.

849 **3 GULDEN 1721, 1764, 1786, 1795-1796 (GELDERS)**

HAC NITIMVR - HANC TVEMVR, female figure with capped spear in one hand leaning on a
pedestal.
MO: ARG: ORD: FOE: BELG: D: GEL: &: C:Z., crowned arms separating 3 - GL.

1850 [224]   3 GULDEN N.D., 1763-1764, 1791-1792, 1795, 1800 (HOLLAND

Similar to #1849.
Similar to #1849 with FAED and ending HOLL: value 3 - G

1851   3 GULDEN 1721 (OVERIJSSEL)

Similar to #1849 with date .1721. not under a bar.
Similar to #1849 with FAED. and legend ending TRANSI.

1852   3 GULDEN 1714, 1719, 1763-1764, 1785-1786, 1791-1796 (UTRECHT

Similar to #1849.
Similar to #1849 with FOED. and legend ending TRAI.

1853   3 GULDEN 1701, 1703, 1714, 1721, 1763-1764, 1767, 1781, 1786, 1791-1796 (WEST FRIESLAND)

Similar to #1849.
Similar to #1849 with FOE(D). and legend ending WESTF:
Two varieties of the 1714 and three of the 1795.

MAASTRICHT

1854   100 STIVERS 1794

Four punches: 1794 in box, double lined star, 100 ST. in box, and LE.
TRAIECTUM AD MOSAM spray, star in border.

1855   100 STIVERS 1794

URBE 1794 OBSESSA spray, 100 / STRS. in border.
Similar to #1854.

1856   100 STIVERS 1794
Similar to #1854. Uniface.
A. Punched on a French ecu.

APPENDIX A

Certain frequently repeated abbreviations have not been translated as a matter of economy. These include D.G.—DEI GRATIA, by the grace of God; S.R.I.—SACRI ROMANI IMPERII, of the Holy Roman Empire; and R.I. or R.I.S.A.—ROMANORUM IMPERATOR SEMPER AUGUSTUS—Emperor of the Romans, ever august. Some proper names have been arbitrarily translated—CAROLUS as Charles, Karl, or Carlo, for instance, depending on the country. Frederick, John, and Henry likewise appear in several forms.

— A —

A. V. & O. S. Steph. R.A.M.C. Eq. U.S. C.R.A.M.A.I. Cons. Conf. M. & S.A. Praef (1189) Knight both of the Golden Fleece and of the Order of the Great Cross of the Apostolic king St. Stephen, present privy counselor of their sacred, imperial, royal and apostolic majesties, conference minister, and high prefect of the court.

Abb. S.G.E.S.I.A.V.E. (1778,9) Abbot of St. Gallen and St. John, Knight of the Virgin of the Annunciation.

Ad Normam Conventionis (1148,1204) According to the convention standard.

Ad Usam Luxemburgi CC Vallati (1592) For the use of besieged Luxemburg.

Adolphus Frid. D.G. Rex Sveciae (1731-3) Adolf Frederick D.G. king of Sweden.

Adventus Optimi Principis (1473,4) The coming of the noblest prince.

Alle Speranze della Gioventu La Patria (1483) For the hope of the youth, the Fatherland.

Aloy(i)sio(i) Mocenico Duce (1562,3) Alvise Mocenigo doge.

Aloysius Mocenigo Dux Venetiar (1524, 35,57) Alvise Mocenigo, doge of Venice.

Aloysius Pisani Dux Venetiar (1541) Alvise Pisani, doge of Venice.

Andreas D.G. Arch. et Princeps Salis. S.A.L. (1245,6) Andreas D.G. archbishop and prince of Salzburg, legate of the Apostolic See.

Anna Dei Gratia (1338-44) Anna D.G.

Anno Dni. MDCCIX et Regiminis Primo F.F. (1235) In the year of our Lord 1709 and the first year of the reign.

Anno I della Liberta Italiana (1576,7) The first year of Italian liberty.

Anno settimo della Liberta (1410) The seventh year of liberty

Ant. I. D.G. Prin. Monoegi (1612) Antonio I D.G. Prince of Monaco

Ant. Ptolom. Trivultius (1482) Antonio Tolomeo Trivulzio

Ant. Theodor D.G. Prim. A. Ep. Olomu. Dux (1233) Anton Theodor D.G. first archbishop of Olmütz, duke

Antoni Ioh. S.R.I. Com. de Nost. et Rin. (1191) Anton Johann S.R.I. count of Nostitz and Rieneck

Antonius I Barbiani Belgiojoso et S.R.I. Princeps (1356) Antonio I Barbiani of Belgiojoso, prince S.R.I.

Apres les tenebres la lumiere (1768) After the shadows, the light

Aragonum Rex (1694) King of Aragon

Ar(c). Au. Dux Bu. Medi. Pr. Tran. Co. Ty. (1144,5) Archduke of Austria, duke of Burgundy and Milan, prince of Transylvania, count of Tyrol

Arch. A.D. Bu. Pr. Tran. N.D. Lo. B.M. D.Etr. (1141-3) Archduchess of Austria, duchess of Burgundy, princess of Transylvania, married to the duke of Lorraine, Bar, grandduke of Tuscany

Arch. Aus(t). Dux Burg. Brab. C. Fl. (1280-2) Archduke of Austria, duke of Burgundy and Brabant, count of Flanders

Arch. Aust. Dux Burg. C. Fland. (1270) Archduke of Austria, duke of Burgundy, count of Flanders

Arch. Aust. Dux Bu. et Mantuae (1378) Archduke of Austria, duke of Burgundy and Mantua

Arch. Aust. Dux Burg Loth. Brab. Com. Flan. (1170,5,80,1284,6,1388,9,90) Archduke of Austria, duke of Burgundy, Lorraine, Brabant, count of Flanders

Arch(idux) Aust. D(ux) Burg. (et) Loth. M(ag) D(ux) Het(r). (1161-7, 71, 3,6,8) Archduke of Austria, duke of Burgundy and Lorraine, grandduke of Tuscany

Archi. Monetar(ius) Haereditari Utriusq. (Archiducat) Austriae (1198,9) Chief moneyer of both the hereditary archduchies of Austria

Archid. Au. D. Bu. M. Mor. Co. Ty. (1079-83) Archduke of Austria, duke of Burgundy, margrave of Moravia, count of Tyrol

Archid. Aust. Dux Burg. Braban(t) (1268,9,78,9,1702-4) Archduke of Austria, duke of Burgundy and Brabant

Archid. Aust. Dux Burg. et Siles. Marg. Mor. (1065,8-73,5,6,8,1136) Archduke of Austria, duke of Burgundy and Silesia, margave of Moravia

Archid. Aus(triae) Dux Burg (et) Styriae (etc) (1002,15,39-43,1118,9) Archduke of Austria, duke of Burgundy and Styria etc.

Archid. Aust. D. Burg. Marggr. Burgo- viae (1148) Archduke of Austria, duke of Burgundy, margrave of Burgau

Archid(ux) Aust(riae) Dux Bur(gun- diae) Com. Ty(rolis) (1001,3,13-16,8, 35-38, 49-56, 84-87, 1107, 9-12, 14-16, 17, 20-24, 38-40, 6,7,9,50,1) Archduke of Austria, duke of Burgundy, count of Tyrol

Archid(ux) Aus. Dux Bur. Mar. Mor. Co. Tyr. (1004,5, 19-23, 57-63, 1110) Arch- duke of Austria, duke of Burgundy, margrave of Moravia, count of Tyrol.

Archidux Aust. Dux Burg. Princ. Trans- syl. (1101-4,6) Archduke of Austria, duke of Burgundy, prince of Transyl- vania

Archidux Austriae (1033,4) Archduke of Austria

Archidux Austriae Dux Burg(u) et(&) Silesiae (1009-11,28-31,94-98) Arch- duke of Austria, duke of Burgundy and Silesia

Archiep. Vien. S.R.I.P. Ep. Vacien, Adm. S. Steph. R.A.M.C.E. (1267) Arch- bishop of Vienna, prince S.R.I., ad- ministrator of Waitzen bishopric, knight of the Grand Cross of the Apostolic King St. Stephen

Auxilium de Sancto (1471,2,88) Aid from the Sanctuary

Auxilium Meum A. Domino (1612) My help (cometh) from the Lord

Augustus II D.G. Rex Pol(oniarum) M. D(ux) Lit. D. Sax. I.C.M.A.& W. (1613-5) August II D.G. king of Po- land, grandduke of Lithuania, duke of Saxony, Jülich, Cleves, Berg, Angria, and Westphalia

Avr. Vell. Equ. S.C. & Cat. Mai. Intim. & Conferent. Consiliar. (1201) Knight of the Golden Fleece, privy and con- ference chancellor of their sacred, im- perial and Catholic majesties

Avr. Vel. Equ. SS.CC.RR.MM. Act. Int. et Conferent. Consil. et Supr. Camer. (1188) Knight of the Golden Fleece, present privy and conference chancel- lor of their sacred, imperial, royal majesties, and High Chamberlain

— B —

B. Nicolaus de Flue. Helv. Cath. Patr. (1780) Blessed Nicholas of Flue, pa- tron of Catholic Switzerland

Barbarae Qvirini Sponsae Dulcissimae Moribvs Ingenio Praeclarae Intem- pestiva Morte Perempte Die XXIII Oct. Thomas Obicivs Moerens Memo- riam Perennat A.S. MDCCXCVI (1427) To his betrothed Barbara Quirini, most sweet in character and illustrious in her genius, carried away

by untimely death on the 23rd day of October, Thomas Obizzi in grief honors her memory.

Basilic. Liber. (1433-5) The Church of Liberius

Basilea (1741,3-5,7-53,5-7) Basel

Beda D.G. S.R.I.P. (1778-9) Beda D.G. prince S.R.I.

Bened. XIV Pont. Max. (1459) Benedict XIV Pope

Benedict(us) XIV P.M. Bonon(iensis) (1457,60,1) Benedict XIV, Pope, of Bologna

Benedict XIV P.M. et Arch. Bon. (1458) Benedict XIV, Pope and archbishop of Bologna

Bey Gott ist Rath und That (1185) There is counsel and action in Our Lord

Bononia Docet (1444,50-2,4,7) Bologna teaches

Brun. et L. Dux S.R.I.A. Th. et El. (1345-6) Duke of Brunswick and Lüne- burg, archtreasurer and elector of S.R.I.

Burgund. Dux Braban(t) (1705-09,11) Duke of Burgundy and Brabant

Burgund. Dux C. Fland. (1710) Duke of Burgundy, count of Flanders

— C —

C.P.R.S.R.I.A.El. & Vic. LL. C.F.H. & N.M.S.R.I.D. Mech. (1271,3,5,7) Count Palatine of the Rhine, archsteward and elector and regent of SR.I., land- grave of Leuchtenberg, count of Flan- ders, Hainaut, and Namur, margrave of S.R.I., lord of Mechlin

Caes. d'Avalos de Aquino de Arag. Mar. Pis. et Vasti D.G.S.R.I.Pr. (1523) Ce- sare D'Avalos of Aquino of Aragon, marquis of Pescara and Vasto, D.G. prince of S.R.I.

Capitulum Brixense Regnans Sede Va- cante (1204) The Chapter of Brixen governing, the seat being vacant

Car. & Amal. Philipp Popul. Spes Nat. A. 1747 (1398) Charles and Amalie, Philip the hope of the people, born year 1747

Car. D.G. Rex Nea(p). Hisp. Infans (1397,9) Charles D.G. king of Naples, prince of Spain

Car. D.G. Utr. Sic. et Hier. Rex (1400) Charles D.G. king of the Two Sicilies and Jerusalem

Car. Em. D.G. Rex Sar. Cyp. et Ier. (1493-5) Charles Emanuele D.G. king of Sardinia, Cyprus, and Jerusalem.

Car. Lud. S.R.I. Com. a Dietrichstain (1186) Karl Ludwig S.R.I. count of Dietrichstein

Car. Utr. Sic. & Mar. Amal. Reg. (1398) Charles, king of the Two Sicilies, and Maria Amalie queen

Car(ol) VI D.G. Rom. Imp(e) (1395,6) Karl VI D.G. Roman Emperor

Carlini Dodeci (1410) Twelve carlini

Carol. Frider. D.G.H.N. Dux Sles. et Ho . (1352) Karl Friedrich D.G. heir of Norway, duke of Schleswig-Holstein

Carol S.R.I. Princ. de Batthyan. P.I.N.U. & S. Com. Aur. V.E.C.C.P.S.U.S.C. (1182) Karl, S.R.I., prince of Batthyani, hereditary count in Nemet-Ujvar and Siklos, knight of the Golden Fleece, hereditary in the county of Eisenburg, full supreme count of Simega (Somogy)

Carol S.R.I. Princ. de Batthyan. P.I.N.U. & S. Com. Aur. V.et Ord. S. Steph. R.A. Magn. Cruc. Eques. C.C.P.S.VS.C. (1183) as preceding, knight of the Golden Fleece and of the Order of the Grand Cross of the Apostolic King St. Stephen, hereditary in the county of Eisenburg, full supreme count of Simega

Carol III D.G. (1412) Charles III D.G.

Carol III D.G. Sicil et Hier. Rex (1413, 4) Charles III D.G. king of Sicily and Jerusalem

Carol VI D.G. (Ro(m). Imp. S.A. Ger(m). Hisp. Hu(ng) (et) Bo(h). Rex (1035-65,68-87,89-1104,6,7,95,1378) Karl VI D.G. R.I.S.A., king of Germany, Spain, Hungary, and Bohemia

Carolus D.G. Sic. et Hier. Rex Hisp. Inf. (1415) Charles D.G., king of Sicily and Jerusalem, prince of Spain

Carolus Ruzini Dux Venetiar. (1538) Carlo Ruzzini, doge of Venice

Carolus III D(ei) G(ratia) (1411, 1699, 1700) Charles III D.G.

Carolus III D.G. Hisp. et Indiarum Rex (1268-70) Charles III D.G. king of Spain and the Indies

Carolus III Rex Hispaniarum (1380) Charles III king of Spain

Carolus IIII Dei G. (1701) Charles IV D.G.

Carolus VI D.G. Imp. et His. Rex (1381-2) Karl VI, emperor and king of Spain

Carolus VI D.G. Rom. Imp. Hisp. et Ind. Rex (1278-9) Karl VI D.G. R.I. king of Spain and the Indies

Carolus VI D.G. Rom (Imp(er). S(emp). A(u). (1066,7,88,1761) Karl VI D.G. R.I.S.A.

Carolus XII D.G. Rex Sve(ciae) (etc) (1712-6) Charles XII D.G. king of Sweden etc.

Casparus Ignatius D.G. Episcop. (1203) Caspar Ignatz D.G. bishop

Christ(ianus) VI D.G. Rex Dan. Norv. V.G. (1294,5,7) Christian VI D.G. king of Denmark, Norway, Vendalia, Gothland

Christ. VII D.G. Rex Dan. Nor. Van. Got. (1305) Christian VII then as above

Christian den VII Danmarks og Norges Konge (1312) Christian VII king of Denmark and Norway

Christianus VII D.G. Dan. Norv. V.G. Rex (1311,3-5) Christian VII D.G. king of Denmark, Norway, Vendalia, Gothland

Christophorus D.M.S.R.E. Cardinalis de Migazzi (1267) Christopher, by the mercy of God, Cardinal Migazzi of the Holy Roman Church

Civibus Quorum Pietas Coniuratione Die III Mai MDCCXCI Obrutan et Deletam Libertate Polona Tueri Conabatur Respublica Resurgens (1622) To the citizens whose piety the resurgent commonwealth tried to protect. Poland overturned and deprived of liberty by the conspiracy of the 3rd day of May 1791

Clemens XI P(ont). M(ax). (1428-49) Clement XI Pope

Clemens XII Pont. Max. (1455) Clement XII Pope

Clemens XIII Pont. Max. (1463) Clement XIII Pope

Coeli Regina Rp. Rhac. Patrona (1638) Queenof Heaven, patron of the Republic of Ragusa

Com. in Theng. S.C.M. Intim. Cons. et Supr. Stabuli Praefect (1181) Count of Thengen, privy counselor of his sacred, imperial majesty and High Constable

Com. P.R.S.R.I.Ar. & Ele. LL. Com. F.H. & N. Mar. S.R.I.D.M. (1272,4,6) Count Palatine of the Rhine, archsteward and elector of S.R.I. landgrave of Leuchtenberg, count of Flanders, Hainaut, and Namur, margrave of S.R.I., lord of Mechlin

Comes Cunii Lugi March. Grumelli (1356) Count of Cuneo, Lugio, marquis of Grumellio

Comunitas et Senatus Bonon. (1357) The city and the Senate of Bologna

Concordia res parvae crescunt (1823-48) By concord small things increase

Confidens Dno. Non. Movetur (1821-2) Who trusts in the Lord is not moved

Constantia et Labore (1352) By steadfastness and toil

Constantia et Labore (1352) By steadfastness and toil

Convenienta Cuique (1377) For everyone's convenience

Cosmos III D.G. M(ag). Dux Etruriae VI (1498-1501) Cosmo III D.G. sixth grandduke of Tuscany

— D —

D.G. Archiepiscop.& S.R.I. Princ. Salisburg S.S.A.L. (1237,9) D.G. Archbishop of Salzburg and prince of S.R.I., legate of the Holy Apostolic See

D.G. Augustus III Rex Poloniarum (1617) D.G. August III, king of Poland

D.G. Carolus Epus. Olomucen. (1205-6) D.G. Karl bishop of Olmütz

D.G. Carolus Episcopus Olomucensis (1207,12) same as above

D.G. Dan. Nor(v). Van(d). Got(h). Rex (1304,6,7,8) D.G. king of Denmark, Norway, Vendalia, Gothland

D.G. Parmae Plac(et). Vast. Dux (1479-81) D.G. Duke of Parma, Piacenza and Guastalla

D.G. Petrus in Liv. Curl. et Semgal. Dux (1624) D.G. Peter, duke of Livonia, Curland, and Semigalia

D.G. Rex Dan. Nor(v). Va(n). Got(t). (1292,6) D.G. king of Denmark, Norway, Vendalia, Gothland

D.G. Rex Dan. Nor. Van. Go. Dux Sl. Hols. St. Dit. & Old. (1309) D.G. king of Denmark, Norway, Vendalia, Gothland, duke of Schleswig-Holstein, Stormark, Ditmarsh, and Oldenburg

D. in Furst(enberg) et Furstenav ex L.B. de Rost (1762-4) Lord in Fürstenberg and Fürstenau, late free baron von Rost

Dal. Cro. Sclav. Rex Archid. Aust. D. Burgun. (1064) King of Dalmatia, Croatia, Slavonia, archduke of Austria, duke of Burgundy

Dan. Nor. Van. Got. Rex (1300) King of Denmark, Norway, Vendalia, Gothland

De Socio Princeps (1397,9) A prince from an ally

Decreto Reipublicae Nexu Confederationis Iunctae die V Xbris MDCCXCII Stanislao Augusto Regnante (1622) By decree of the state in conjunction with the joint federation on the 5th day of Dec. 1792, Stanislaus August ruling

Defluit et influit (1449) It flows down and flows in

Dei Gratia Carolus Episcopus Olomucensis (1203-11,3) D.G. Karl bishop of Olmütz

Dextera Domini Exaltavit Me (1394, 1695) The right hand of the Lord has exalted me

Dilexi Decorem Domus Tuae (1429) I have loved the beauty of thy house

Dirige Domine Gressos Meos (1508-11, 14-20) Direct, O Lord, my steps

Divina Per Te Ope (1535-6) With divine help thru thee

Dominabitur Gentium et Ipse (1285) He himself too will be lord of the nation

Domini Conserva Nos in Pace (1740-58, 81-2,4,5,7-91,9) Lord, preserve us in peace

Domini est Regnum (1285) The kingdom is the Lord's

Dominus elegit Te Hodie (1430) The Lord has chosen thee this day

Dominus Mihi Adiutor (1287,90-2) The Lord is my help

Dominus Protector Meus (1712,17) The Lord is my defender

Dominus providebit (1759-60) The Lord will provide

Dominus regit Me (1523) The Lord guides me

Dominus Spes Populi Sui (1775) The Lord, the hope of his people

Dona Nobis Pacem (1437) Give peace to us

Ducat et Sem. Reip. Rhac(v). (1635-7, 9) 1½ ducats of the republic of Ragusa

Ducatus Venetus (1526,7,32,3,7,40,3,6,7, 50,1,5,60,1,6,7,73,4) Ducat of Venice

Duce Deo Fide et Iust. (1640-1) Faith and Justice with God our guide

Dux Burgundiae Comes Tirol (1017) Duke of Burgundy, count of Tyrol

Dux et Gub(ernatores) Reip. Gen(u). (1360-70) Doge and governors of the republic of Genoa

Dux Lothar & (et) Bar. S.R.I. P(cp) .S.R(e).C(a).B(o).Com(es) (1205-9,11-13) Duke of Lorraine and Bar, prince of S.R.I., count of the Royal Chapel of Bohemia

Dux S.R.I. Pcps. Reg. Cap. Bohem. Comes (1215) Duke, prince of S.R.I. count of the Royal Chapel of Bohemia

Dux S.R.I.P.R.C.B.C. Protec. Ger. S.C.R. M. Con. in et Ac. (1219) like preceding, then Protector of Germany, privy and present counselor of his sacred, imperial, royal majesty

Dux S.R.I.PS.R.C.B. Com. Con. Ger. S.C. R.M. Con in et Actu. (1216-8) same as preceding except Counselor for Protector

Dux Sab(aud) et Montisf(er). Princ. Ped(em) (1493-7) Duke of Savoy and Montferrat, prince of Piedmont

Dux Sax. I.C.M.A.& W. Elect. (1614-5) Duke of Saxony, Jülich, Cleves, Berg, Angria, and Westphalia, elector

Dux Sles. Hol(s). Stor(m). Ditm. Com. Old. (et) Del(m). (1288,93) Duke of Schleswig-Holstein, Stormark, Ditmarsh, count of Oldenburg and Delmenhorst

— E —

E. P. Le. D. Bul. C.L. Ho. M. Fra. (1581) Prince bishop of Liege, duke of Bouillon, count of Looz, Horn, Marquis of Franchimont

Egalite Liberte Independence (1768) Equality, liberty, independence

Ein Thaler nach den Reichs Fus (1355-6) A taler after the imperial standard

Elisabetha I. D.G. Imp. Tot. Ross. (1960) Elizabeth I D.G. empress of all Russia

Emitte Coelitus Lucis Tuae Radium (1456) Send forth a ray of heavenly light

Epis. Basileensis S.R.I. Prince (1739) Bishop of Basel, prince of S.R.I.

Episc. Olom. Dux S.R.I. Princ. Reg. Cap. Boh. Com. (1232) Bishop and duke of Olmütz, prince of S.R.I., and count of the Royal Chapel of Bohemia

Et Patet et Favet (1498,1500,2) It is both evident and favorable

Et Polestinae Princ. Ardoris et Sac. Romani Imp. (1491) And Polistina, prince of Ardore and S.R.I.

Et Praesidium et Decus (1638) Both defense and glory

Et Rege Eos (1360-6,8) And rule them

Et S.R.I. Princeps Brixinensis (1203) And prince of S.R.I. and Brixen

Ex Avro Argentea resurgit (1414,6,20,2) From gold it arises, again silver

— F —

F.D. An. Manoel de Vilhena (1593-7) Brother Don Antony Manoel de Vilhena

F.D. Emmanual Pinto (1599) Brother Don Emanuel Pinto

F.D. Raimun(dus) Despuyg M.M.H.H. (1598) Brother Don Raymund Despuig, Grand Master of the Hospital of Jerusalem

F. Emmanuel de Rohan M.M. (H.SS.) (1606-10) Brother Emanuel de Rohan, Grand Master of the Hospital and the Holy Sepulchre

F. Emmanuel Pinto M.M.H.S.S. (1600-4) Brother Emanuel Pinto, Grand Master of the Hospital and the Holy Sepulchre

F. Ferdinandus Hompesch M.M. (1611) Brother Ferdinand Hompesch, Grand Master

Faderneslandet (1734-6) The Fatherland

Fausto Coronationis (1415) A happy augury for the crowning

Fecunditas (1403) Fertility

Ferd. Car. D.G. Dux Mant. Mont. Car. Guas. (1337) Ferdinand Charles D.G. duke of Mantua, Montferrat, Carolivilla, Guastalla

Ferd. Iul. D.G.S.R.E. Cardin. de Troyer (1232) Ferdinand Julius D.G. Cardinal de Troyer of the Holy Roman Church

Ferdin. Iul. D.G. Episc. Olomuc. Dux S.R.I.Pr. (1231) Ferdinand Julius D.G. Bishop of Olmütz, duke, prince of the S.R.I.

Ferdinan(dus) D.G. Sicil. et Hier. Rex 1416,7-25) Ferdinand D.G. king of Sicily and Jerusalem

Ferdinandus Rex Maria Carolina Regina (1403) Ferdinand king, Maria Carolina queen

Ferdinandus I Hisp. Infans (1479-81) Ferdinand I, prince of Spain

Ferdinandus III D.G.P.R.H. et B.A.A. M.D. Etrur. (1521) Ferdinand III, royal prince of Hungary and Bohemia, archduke of Austria, grand duke of Tuscany

Ferdinan(dus) IV D.G. Siciliar et Hier. Rex (1401,24,5,6,9) Ferdinand IV D.G. king of Sicily and Jerusalem

Ferdinandus IV et M. Carolina Undiq. Felices (1408) Ferdinand IV and Maria Carolina, blessed on all sides

Ferdinandus IV et Maria Carolina (1407) Ferdinand IV and Maria Carolina

Ferdinandus IV Neap. et Sic. Rex (1489) Ferdinand IV, king of Naples and Sicily

Ferdinandus IV Utr. Sic. Rex (1488) Ferdinand IV, king of the Two Sicilies

Fiat Pax in Virtute Tua (1438,41) Let there be peace in Thy strength

Fides et Victoria (1538,34) Faith and victory

Firmata Securitas (1398) Estab. safety

Firmissimum Libertatis Munimentum (1367) The strongest memorial of freedom

Foedus est inter me et te (1455) There is a covenant between me and thee

Fontis et Fori Ornamen(to) (1445-6) An ornament to the fountain and the forum

Fr. D. Franciscus Ximenez de Texada (1605) Brother Don Francisco Ximenez de Texada

Fr. Ios. Max. Pr. de Lobk. Dux Raud. Pr. Com. in Sternst. (1190) Franz Josef Maximilian, prince of Lobkowitz, duke of Raudnitz, prince, count in Sternstein

Franc. Ant. S.R.I. Princ ab Harrach (1239) Franz Anton, prince von Harrach of the S.R.I.

Franc. Anto. D.G. Archi. et Pr. Salisb. S.S.A.L.Pr. de Har. (1235) Franz Anton D.G. archbishop and prince of Salzburg, legate of the Holy Apostolic See, prince von Harrach

Franc. Anto. D.G. Arch. Pr. Sal. S.A.L. (1236,8) Franz Anton D.G. prince archbishop of Salzburg, legate of the Apostolic See

Franc. D.G. Hu. Bo. Ga. Lod. Rex A.A. D.B. et L.M.D. Hetr. (1177) Franz D.G. king of Hungary, Bohemia, Galicia, Lodomeria, archduke of Austria, duke of Burgundy and Lorraine, grand duke of Tuscany

Franc. D.G. R(o). I.S.A. Ge. Ier. R. Lo. B.M.H.D. (1152-60) Franz D.G. R.I.S. A., king of Germany and Jerusalem, Lorraine, Bar, grand duke of Tuscany

Franc. Euseb. Trauthson Com. in Falkenstain (1200) Franz Eusebius of Trautson, count in Falkenstein

Franc. Gund. S.R.I.P. Colloredo Mannsfeld C. in Walds. V.C. in Mels M. in S. Soph. S.R.I. Pro. Canc. (1185) Franz Gundacker, prince of S.R.I. of Colloredo-Mannsfeld, count in Waldsee, viscount of Mels, marquis of St. Sophia, vice chancellor of S.R.I.

Franc. Hen. Schlik S.R.I.C. de Passano & Weiskerchen (1196) Franz Heinrich count of S.R.I. of Schlick, Passaun and Weiskirchen

Franc. Ignat. S.R.I.C. & Dom. de et in Sprinzenstein et Neuhaus (1198) Franz Ignatz, count of S.R.I., lord of Sprinzenstein and Neuhaus

Franz. Ios. D.G.S.R.I.Pr. & Gub. Dom. de Liechtenstein (1580) Franz Joseph D.G. prince of S.R.I., ruling lord of Liechtenstein

Franc. Ios. Schlick Com. a Bassan. & Weisk. (1195) Franz Joseph, count of Schlick, Passaun, and Weiskirchen

Franc Lauredano Duce (1552) Francisco Lauredano, doge

Franc Lavredano Dux Venetiar (1548) Francisco Lauredano, doge of Venice

Franc. II D.G.R. Imp. S.A. Ge. Hu. Bo. Rex A.A.D.B.L.M.D.H. (1179) Franz II D.G. R.I.S.A., king of Germany, Hungary, Bohemia, archduke of Austria, duke of Burgundy and Lorraine. grand duke of Tuscany

Franc. II D.G.R. Imp. S.A. Ger. Hier. Hung. Boh. Rex (1286) Franz II D.G. R.I.S.A., king of Germany, Jerusalem, Hungary, Bohemia

Francis D. Gratia Roman Imperat. S.A. (1283) Franz II D.G. R.I.S.A.

Francisc. II D.G.R.I.S.A. Ger. Hie. Hun. Boh. Rex (1390) Franz II D.G. R.I. S.A., king of Germany, Jerusalem, Hungary, Bohemia

Francis(cus) Anto(n) S.R.I. Princ. de Harrach (1237) Franz Anton, prince of S.R.I. of Harrach

Franciscus D.G.R.I.S.A. G.H(ier). Rex Lot(h). Bar M.D. Etr. (1504-7) Franz D.G. R.I.S.A., king of Germany and Jerusalem, Lorraine, Bar, grand duke of Tuscany

Franciscus D.G. Hungar. Bohem. Gallic. Lodom. Rex (1176) Franz D.G. king of Hungary, Bohemia, Galicia, Lodomeria

Franciscus Ursin. S.R.I. Princeps Rosenberg (1192) Franz Orsini, prince of S.R.I. of Rosenberg

Franciscus II D.G.R. Imp. S.A. Germ. (Hie). Hu(n) Bo(h). Rex (1178,80) Franz II D.G. R.I.S.A., king of Germany, Jerusalem, Hungary, Bohemia

Franciscus III Mut. Reg. Mir. Dux (1392) Francis III, duke of Modena, Reggio, and Mirandola

Frid. D.G. Rex Bor. et El. S. Pr. Ar. Neoc. et Val. (1776) Friedrich D.G. king and elector of Prussia, supreme prince of Arausonia, Neuchatel, and Valangin

Frid. Wilh. D.G. Rex Bor. et El. S. Pr. Ar. Neoc. & Val. (1777) Friedrich Wilhelm, then as preceding

Frid. IIII D.G. Dan. Norv. Va(n). Go(t). Rex (1287-8) Frederik IV D.G. king of Denmark, Norway, Vendalia, Gothland

Frideric(us) et Ulr. Eleon. D.G. Rex et Reg. Svec(iae) (1721,2,4,5) Frederik and Ulrica Eleonora D.G. king and queen of Sweden

Fridericus Carolus D.G.H.N.D.S.H.S. et D.C. in O. et D. (1354-5) Frederick Karl D.G. heir of Norway, duke of Schleswig-Holstein, Stormark and Ditmarch, count in Oldenburg and Delmenhorst

Fridericus D.G. Rex Sveciae (1719,20, 3,6-9,30) Frederik D.G. king of Sweden

Frid(ericus) IIII (IV) D.G. Rex Dan. Nor. V. G(o). (1289,90,3) Frederik IV D.G. king of Denmark, Norway, Vendalia, Gothland

Fridericus V D.G. Dan. Nor. V(an). G(ot). Rex (1302-3) same as preceding except for V

Fridericus V D.G. Rex Dan. Nor. V(and). G. (1297-9,1301-2) same as preceding

Fridericus V Dei Gratia (1300) Frederik V D.G.

Fyra Caroliner (1717) Four caroliners

— G —

Gen. C. Mar. V.L. Dim. Col. U.S.C. & R.A.M.A.I. Cons. & S. Conf. M. (1182-3) General field marshal, colonel of the only dragoon regiment, present privy counselor of both their sacred, imperial and royal apostolic majesties, and state conference minister

Geneve Republique (1769-70) Republic of Geneva

Georgius D.G.M. Br. Fr. et Hib. Rex F.D. (1345-6) George D.G. king of Great Britain, France and Ireland, Defender of the Faith

Georgius II Dei Gratia (1347-51) George II D.G.

Germ. Hispa. Hun(g). et Bohemiae Rex (1066,7,88) King of Germany, Spain, Hungary, and Bohemia

Germ(an). Hung(ar). et Bohemiae Rex (1006-8,24-27) King of Germany, Hungary, and Bohemia

Germ. Jero. Rex Loth. Bar. Mag. Het. Dux (1283) King of Germany, Jerusalem, Lorraine, Bar, grand duke of Tuscany

Giorno che vale di tanti anni il pianto (1484-5) The day which is worth so many years of sorrow

Gloria ex Amore Patriae (1304-10) Glory from love of country

Gratia obvia ultio quaestia Liburni (1499, 1501,3) Grace proffered, punishment provoked, Livorno (Leghorn)

Gratitudo concivibus exemplum posteritati (1622) Gratitude to fellow citizens, an example to posterity

Gud mitt Hopp (1718,20,3,7-30) God my hope

Gud och Folket (1737-8) God and the people

Gud wart Hopp (1721,2,4) God our hope

Gustaf IV Aldolph Sv. G. och W. Konung (1727-8) Gustaf IV, king of Sweden, Gothland, and Vendalia

Gustavus III D.G. Rex Sveciae (1734-6) Gustaf III, king of Sweden

— H —

Haer. Norw. Dux Slesv. Hols. St. & Ditm. Com. Old. & Delm. (1353) Heir of Norway, duke of Schleswig-Holstein, Stormark, Ditmarsh, count of Oldenburg and Delmenhorst

Hanc tuemur, hac nitimur (1849-53) This we defend, by this we strive

Helvet(ische) Republ(ik) (1771-3) Helvetian Republic

Henricus S.R.I. Princeps Avrsperg Dux Minsterberg (1181) Henry, prince of S.R.I. of Auersperg, duke of Münsterberg

Hercules III D.G. Mut. Reg. Mir. Ec. Dux (1393-4) Ercole III D.G. duke of Modena, Reggio and Mirandola

Hieronymus D.G.A. & P.S.A.S.L.N.G. Prim. (1262-6) Jerome D.G. archbishop and prince of Salzburg, legate of the Apostolic See, born Primate of Germany

Hisp. Utr. Sici. Rex (1395) King of Spain and the Two Sicilies

Hispan(iarum) Infans (1400-2,4-6,9,17-9,21,3-5) Prince of Spain

Hispaniarum Rex (1692,3,6-1701) King of Spain

Hospita(lis) et S. Sep(ul) Hierus(al) (1607-9,11) Hospital and Holy Sepulchre of Jerusalem

— I —

Iac. Ern. D.G. Epus. Olomucensis Dux S.R.I. Pcps. (Spcp) (1227-30) Jacob Ernst, D.G. bishop of Olmütz, duke, prince of S.R.I.

Iacobus Ernst D.G. Arch. & Princ. Salis. S.A.L. (1243-4) Jacob Ernst, D.G. archbishop and prince of Salzburg, legate of the Apostolic See

Immortale Decus Virtutis Avitae (1372) Immortal glory of the virtue of the forefathers

In Hoc Signo Vinces (1625-33) In this sign thou shalt conquer

In Honorem S. Theodori Mar. (1431) In honor of St. Theodore, martyr

In Memor. Vindicatae Libert. ac Relig. (1719) In honor of vindicated liberty and religion

In Te Domini Speravi (1152-60, 1504-7, 12,3) In Thee, O Lord, have I hoped

In Testimonia Tua et non in Avaritiam (1440) To Thy laws and not to avarice

Innocent(ius) XIII Pon(t). M(ax). (1450-2) Innocent XIII Pope

Insignia Capituli Brixinensis (1204) The insignia of the Chapter of Brixen

Io. Ernest D.G. Archiep. Sal. S.A.L. (1234) Johann Ernst D.G. archbishop of Salzburg, legate of the Apostolic See

Io. Ios. Kevenhuller ab Aichelberg S.R.I. Pr. A. Metsch (1189) Johann Josef Khevenhüller of Aichelberg, Prince of S.R.I. of Metsch

Io. Ios.S.R.I. Com. A. Kevenhuller Metsch in Osterwiz (1188) Johann Josef, count of S.R.I. of Khevenhüller-Metsch in Osterwitz

Io. Leop. S.R.I. Princeps Trautson Com. in Falkenstein (1201) Johann Leopold, prince of S.R.I. of Trautson, count in Falkenstein

Ioan. Dominic Milano D.G.S.R.I. (1490) John Dominic Milano, D.G. prince of S.R.I.

Ioan. Gasto. I D.G. Mag. Dux Etrur. VII (1502) John Gaston I D.G. seventh duke of Tuscany

Ioannes Antonius D.G. Ep. Cur. S.R.I. Pr. (1764,6) Johann Anton D.G. bishop of Chur, prince of S.R.I.

Ioannes Conradus D.G. (1739) Johann Conrad D.G.

Ioannes Cornelio Dux Ven. (1529-30) Giovanni Corner, doge of Venice

Ioannes V D.G. Port. et Alg. Rex (1628) John V, king of Portugal and Algarve

Ioh. Wen. S.R. Imp. Princeps a Paar (1193) Johann Wenzel, prince of S.R.I. of Paar

Ios. Bened. D.G. Episcopus Curiens S.R.I. Princeps (1762-3) Joseph Benedict D.G. bishop of Chur, prince of S.R.I.

Ios. Cle. D.G. Arch. Col. S.R.I.P. El. B.D. (1581) Joseph Clemens D.G. archbishop of Cologne, prince of S.R.I., elector, duke of Bavaria

Ios. Io. Ad. D.G.S.R.I.P. & Gub. Dom. de Liechtenstein (1578) Joseph Johann Adam D.G. prince of S.R.I. and ruling lord of Liechtenstein

Ios. Ma. Gon. Guas. Sab. Dux Boz. Prin. (1372) Joseph Maria Gonzaga, duke of Guastalla and Sabbioneta, prince of Bozzolo

Ios. Wenc. D.G.S.R.I. Pr. & Gub. Dom. de Liechtenstein (1579) Joseph Wenceslaus D.G. prince of S.R.I., and ruling lord in Liechtenstein

Ios. II D.G.R.I(mp). S.A.G.H.B.R(ex) A.A.D.B. et(&) L. (1168-9) Joseph II D.G.R.I.S.A., king of Germany, Hungary, Bohemia, archduke of Austria, duke of Burgundy and Lorraine

Ioseph II D.G.R.I.S.A. Cor. Her. R.H.B. (1161-6) Joseph II D.G. R.I.S.A. coregent and heir of the kingdoms of Hungary and Bohemia

Ioseph II D.G. R.I.S.A. Germ. (Hie.) Hu(n). Bo(h). Rex (1167,70,1388) Joseph II D.G. R.I.S.A. king of Germany, Jerusalem, Hungary, Bohemia

Ioseph II D.G.R. Imp. S.A. Ger. Hier. Hung. Boh. Rex (1284) same as preceding

Ioseph II D.G.R Imp. S. Aug. G.H. et B. Rex A.A. (1387) same as preceding plus archduke of Austria

Iosephus D.G. Roman Imp(er) Semper A(v). (1024-7) Joseph D.G. R.I.S.A.

Iosephus D.G. Ro(m). Imp(erator) S(em) A(u) Ger. Hu. et Bo. Rex (1013-23,28-31,3,4) Joseph D.G. R.I.S.A. king of Germany, Hungary, and Bohemia

Iosephus I D.G. Port. et Alg. Rex (1629) Joseph I D.G. king of Portugal and Algarve

Iosephus II D.G. Rom. Imp. Semp. Aug. (1766) Joseph II D.G. R.I.S.A.

Iustitia et Concordia (1783,6,92-7) Justice and harmony

— J —

Jac. Fr. Milano March. Sanc. Georgii (1491) Giocomo Francesco Milano marquis of San Georgio

Joannes D.G. P. Portugaliae et Alg. (1633) John D.G. prince of Portugal and Algarve

Josephus I D.G. Port. et Alg. Rex (1630) Joseph I D.G. king of Portugal and Algarve

— L —

L.B. in Spreichen. et Schrovenstein (1200) Free baron in Sprechenstein and Schroffenstein

L'an IV de l'egalite (1769) Year four of equality

Leop. Hen. Schlik S.R.I.C. de Passaun & Weiskerchen (1197) Leopold Heinrich, count of S.R.I. of Schlick, of Passaun and Weiskirchen

Leop. II D.G. Hu. Bo. Ga. Lod. Rex A.A.D.B. et L.M.D. Hetr. (1172) Leopold II D.G. king of Hungary, Bohemia, Galicia, Lodomeria, archduke of Austria, duke of Burgundy and Lorraine, grandduke of Tuscany

Leopold Vict. Io. S.R.I. Comes a. Windischgratz (1202) Leopold Viktorin Johann, count- of S.R.I. of Windisch-Grätz

Leopold II D.G. R.I.S.A. Ger. Hie. Hun. Boh. Rex (1389) Leopold II D.G. R.I.S.A., king of Germany, Jerusalem, Hungary, Bohemia

Leopoldus D.G. Arch. et Princeps 2) Leopold D.G. archbishop and ᵔ

Leopoldus D.G. Archi. Pr. Sal. S (1241) as above, and of Salzburg, gate of the Apostolic See

Leopold(us) D.G. Rom. Imp. Sem. A Ger. Hun. et Bo. Rex (1001-5,9-, Leopold D.G. R.I.S.A. king of many, Hungary and Bohemia

Leopoldus D.G. Roman(or) Impera. S (1106-8) Leopold D.G. R.I.S.A.

Leopoldus II D.G. H. et B. Rex A.A.i D.E. (1520) Leopold II D.G. king o. Hungary and Bohemia. archduke of Austria, grandduke of Tuscany

Leopoldus II D.G. Hungar. Bohem. Gallic. Lodom. Rex (1171) Leopold II D.G. king of Hungary, Bohemia, Galicia, Lodomeria

Leopoldus II D.G. R.I.S.A. Ger. H. Rex A.A.M.D. Etr. (1519 II D.G. R.I.S.A. king of Jerusalem, and Hungary, arcı. Austria, grandduke of Tuscany

Leop(oldus) II D.G. R. Imp. S.A. (Hie.) Hu(n). Bo(h). Rex (117. Leopold II D.G. R.I.S.A. king of C many, Jerusalem, Hungary, Bohemi·

Lex tua Veritas (1521) Thy law is ι truth

Liber Baro in Hollenburg (1186) Free baron in Hollenburg

Liberta Eguaglianza (1371,1576-7) Liberty, equality

Liberta Romana XXVII (27) Piovosυ An. VII (1484-5) Roman liberty 27 Rainy month Year 7

Lire Dieci Venete (1576-7) Ten Venetian lire

Louis XVI Roi des Francois (1335) Louis XVI king of the French

Lucensis Respublica (1373-6) Republic of Lucca

Lud. XIIII D.G. Fr. et Nav. Rex (1316-22,4) Louis XIV D.G. king of France and Navarre

Lud. XV D.G. Fr. et Nav Rex (1325-32) Louis XV then as above

Lud. XVI D.G. Fr. et Nav. Rex (1333) Louis XVI then as above

Lud. XVI D.G. Fr. et Na. Re. B.D. (1334) as above and lord of Bearn

Ludovico Manin Duce (1575) Ludovico Manin, doge

Ludovico Manin Dux Venetiar (1569-70) Ludovico Manin, doge of Venice

Ludovicus S.R.I. Princeps de Batthyan. Strattmann (1184) Ludwig, prince of S.R.I. of Batthyani Strattmann

Ludovicus XIIII D.G. Fr. et Nav. Rex (1323) Louis XIV D.G. king of France and Navarre

— M —

˙˙˙˙˙ et H. Rex F.D.B. et L.D.S.R.I.A. ˙˙˙˙˙ E. (1347-51) King of Great Britain, France, and Ireland, Defender of the Faith, duke of Brunswick and Lüneburg, arch-treasurer and elector of S.R.I.

˙˙˙H. et S. Sep. Hier. (1599) Grand-ster of the Hospital and Holy Sepchre of Jerusalem

˙˙˙Magis(ter) Hos(p) et S. S(epul) Hierus(alem) (1593-7) same as above

˙˙˙Theresia D.G. R. Imp. (Ge.) Hu. Bo. Reg. (A.A.) (1111-24,34,6-40,4-51, 96-7, 1385-6) Maria Theresia D.G. R.I. queen of Germany, Hungary, Bohemia, archduchess of Austria

I. Ther. D.G. R.I(mp) G(e). H(u). B(o) R.A.A.D.B.C.T. (1129-32) same ˙˙˙ve, and duchess of Burgundy, ˙˙˙ess of Tyrol

˙˙˙ D.G.R. Imp. Hu. Bo. R.A.A.D. ˙˙˙(1133) same as above without ˙˙˙any

˙˙˙ heresia Nata Non. Iuni (1403) ˙˙˙aria Theresia born June 5

˙˙˙. Br(i). Fra. et Hib. Reg. (1338-44) queen of Great Britain, France and Ireland

˙˙˙ar. Th. D.G. R. Imp. G. Hung. Boh. R. (1280-1) Maria Theresia D.G. R.I. queen of Germany, Hungary, Bohemia

Mar. Theresia D.G.R. Imp. Germ. Hung. Boh. Reg. (1282) same as above

March. Sanc. Georgii & Polistinae (1490) Marquis of San Georgio and Polistina

Marco Foscarino Duce (1556) Marco Foscarino, doge

Marcus Foscarenus Dux Venetiar (1553) Marco Foscarino, doge of Venice

Maria Theresia D.G. Reg. Hung. Boh. (1109-10,25-8,41-3) Maria Theresia D.G. queen of Hungary, Bohemia

Maria Theresia D.G. Reg. Hun(g). Boh. Arch. Aust. (1383-4) same as above and archduchess of Austria

Maria I D.G. Port. et Alg. Regina (1632) Maria I D.G. queen of Portugal and Algarve

Maria I et Petrus III D.G. Port. et Alg. Reges (1631) Maria I and Peter III D.G. rulers of Portugal and Algarve

Max. Emanuel D.G.U.B.S.P.B.LL.& G. Dux (1275-7) Maximilian Emanuel D.G. duke of both Bavarias and the Upper Palatinate, Brabant, Limbург, Luxemburg and Gelders

Max. Emanuel V.B.S.P.B.LL.& G. Dux (1271-4) same without D.G.

Med Gudz Hielp (1713-6) With God's help

Mediolani Dux (1385-6) Duke of Milan

Mediolani Dux et C. (1379-84) Duke of Milan and Others

Mediolani et Mant. Dux (1387) Duke of Milan and Mantua

Memor. Ero Tui Iustina Vir(go) (1525, 31,6,9,42,4,9,54,8,9,65,71,2) I will be mindful of you, Justina, Virgin

Mod. Troskab Dapperhed og Hvad der Giver Aere den Heele Verden Kand. Blant Norske Klipper Laere (1289) Courage, loyalty, bravery, and all that gives honor, the whole world can learn among the mountains of Norway

Mo. Arg. Ord. Foe. Belg. D. Gel. & C.Z. (1849) Silver money of the order of the Belgian Federation, duchy of Gelders, county of Zutphen

Mo. Arg. Ord Faed. Belg. Holl. (1850) same but Holland

Mo. Arg. Ord. Foed. Belg. Trai. (1852) same but Utrecht

Mo. Arg. Ord. Faed. Belg. Transi. (1851) same but Overijssel

Mo. Arg. Ord. Foed. Belg. Westf. (1853) same but West Frisia

Mo. Arg. Pro. Con(foe) Belg. D. Gel. & C.Z. (1837-8) Silver money of the provinces of the Belgian Federation, duchy of Gelders, county of Zutphen

Mo. No. Arg. Con. Foe. Belg. Pro. Hol. (1825-7) New silver money of the Belgian Federation, province of Holland

Mo. No. Arg. Con. Foe. Belg. Pro. Tra. (1831-2) same but Utrecht

Mo. No. Arg. Con. Foe. Belg. Pro. Transi(sulania) (1828-30,41-2) same but Overijssel

Mo. No. Arg. Con. Foe. Belg. Pro. Westf. (1833-4) same but West Frisia

Mo(n) No(v) Arg. Pro. Con. Foe(d). Belg. Com. Ze(e)l. (1835-6,47-8) New silver money of the provinces of the Belgian Federation, county of Zeeland

Mo. No. Arg. Pro. Conf. Belg. D. Gel. & C.Z. (1823-4) same but duchy of Gelders, county of Zutphen

Mo. No. Arg. Pro. Confoe. Belg. (Co.) Hol(l). (1839-40) same but county of Holland

Mo. No. Arg. Pro. Confoe. Belg. Trai. (1843-5) same but Utrecht

Mo. No. Arg. Pro. Confoe. Belg. Westfri. (1846) same but West Frisia

Mon. Arg. Conf. Bel. Pro. Trans. (1821) Silver money of the Belgian Federation, province of Overijssel

Mon. Arg. Pro. Con. Foe. Belg. West F. (1822) Silver money of the provinces of the Belgian Federation, West Frisia

Mon. Nova Arg. Duc. Curl. Ad Normam Tal. Alb. (1624) New silver money, duchy of Courland, according to the Albertus taler standard

Moneta Livoesthonica (1690) Money of Lithuania

Moneta Nov. Arg. Regis Daniae (1310) New silver money of the kingdom of Denmark

Moneta Nova ad Normam Conventionis (1192) New money according to the Convention standard

Moneta Nova Argenti Metalli Fod. Reichstein (1099) New silver money of metal of the Reichstein mine

Moneta Nova Capli. Leod. Sede Vacante (1582-91) New money of the Chapter of Liege, the seat being vacant

Moneta Nova Reipublicae Tigurinae (1781) New money of the Republic of Zürich

Moneta Nova Urbis Basileensis (1740) New money of the City of Basel

Moneta Reipub. Basileensis (1754) Money of the Republic of Basel

Moneta Reipubl. Subsylvaniae Superioris (1780) Money of the Republic of Unterwalden

Moneta Reipublicae Tiguri(nae) (1782, 4,7-91) Money of the Republic of Zürich

Moneta Reipublicae Turicensis (1792-9) same as above

Moneta Reipub. Lucernen (1774) Money of the Republic of Luzern

— N —

Nescit Tarda Molimina (1453) He does not know slow enterprises

Nicol. S.R.I. Princ. Eszterhazy de Galantha Perp. Com. in Frak. (1187) Nikolaus, prince of S.R.I. of Eszerhazy of Galantha, hereditary count of Forchtenstein

Non avrum sed nomen (1442) Not in gold but in his name

Non surrexit major (1369-70,1600-2,4) None greater has arisen

— O —

Oblita ex Avro Argentea Resurgit (1413) Forgotten silver comes forth from gold

Opp. & Carn. Dux C. Ritb. Gran. Hisp. P. Clas. S.C.M. Int. Cons. (1578) Duke of Troppau and Carnovia, count of Rietberg, grandee of Spain first class, privy counselor of his sacred, imperial majesty

Opp. & Carn. Dux Com. Rittb. S.C.M. Cons. Int. & Campi. Mareschal (1579) Duke of Troppau and Carnovia, count of Rietberg, privy counselor of his sacred, imperial majesty, Field Marshal

Opp. & Carn. Dux Com. Rittb. S.C.M. Cons. Int. Aur. Velleris Eques (1580) same as above with Knight of the Golden Fleece instead of Field Marshal

— P —

P. Leop(oldus) D.G. P.R.H. et B.A.A. M.D. E(truriae) (1512-3,5-8) Peter Leopold D.G. royal prince of Hungary and Bohemia, archduke of Austria, grandduke of Tuscany

Parmae Plac. et Vastal. Dux (1478) Duke of Parma, Piacenza and Guastalla

Pastori et Principi Senatus Bononensis (1458) To the pastor and prince, the Senate of Bologna

Patria et Scientiarum Instituto Magnifice Aucto S.P.Q.B. (1461) The Senate and the people of Bologna (honors) him for a greatly improved fatherland and enlarged Institute of Science.

Paulo Rainerio Duce (1568) Paolo Renier, doge

Paulus Rainerius Dux Venetiar (1564) Paolo Renier, doge of Venice

Pcps. Reg. Cap. Bo. et de Liechtenstein Comes (1228) Prince of the Royal Chapel of Bohemia, count of Liechtenstein

Perpetuus in Nemet Vivar S.C.R.A.M. Act. Cam. Inc. Com. Cast. Perp.et Supr. Com. (1184) Hereditary count in Nemt-Ujvar, present chamberlain of his sacred, imperial, royal, apostolic majesty, privy counselor, hereditary and supreme count of Eisenburg

Petrus D.G. Magnus Dux Totius Russiae (1353) Peter D.G. grandduke of all Russia

Petrus Grimani Dux Venetiar (1544) Pietro Grimani, doge of Venice

Petrus Leopoldus D.G. P.R.H. et B.A.A. M.D. Etr(uriae) (1508-11,4) see P. Leop.

Petrus II D.G. Port(ug). et Alg. Rex (1626-7) Peter II D.G. king of Portugal and Algarve

Petrus II D.G. Rex Portug. (1625) Peter II D.G. king of Portugal

Philip V D.G. Hisp. Et Ind. Rex (1695) Philip V D.G. king of Spain and the Indies

Philippus D.G. Hispan. Infans. (1478) Philip D.G. prince of Spain

Philippus V D(ei) G(rat) (1692-4,6-8) Philip V D.G.

Philippus V D.G. Hispan. Rex (1691) Philip V D.G. king of Spain

Philippus V D.G. Hispaniarum et Indiarum Rex (1702-11) Philip V D.G. king of Spain and the Indies

Philippus V Rex Hispaniar. (1379) Philip V king of Spain

Pius Sextus Pont. M(ax). (1471-4) Pius VI Pope

Pius VI Pon(t). Max. (1466,8-70,5) Pius VI Pope

Pius VI Pont. Max. Anno Iubeliae (1467) Pius VI Pope, Jubilee year

Pons Civit. Castellana (1443) The bridge of Castellana

Populus et Senatus Bon(on). (1258-9) The people and Senate of Bologna

Portam Sanctam Clausit a Iubilei (1428) He closed the Holy Door in the year of Jubilee

Post Tenebras Lux (1767,9,70) After darkness light

Praesidium et Decus (1357-9) Protection and ornament

Prin. Pede. Rex Cypri. (1492) Prince of Piedmont, king of Cyprus

Prix du Travail (1768) Reward of labor

Pro Fausio PP. Reditur V.S. (1407) For happy returns of the princes of the Two Sicilies

Prosperum iter faciet (1443) It will make the way prosperous

Protectione Virtute (1691) By protection, by valor

Protector noster aspice (1391) Our Protector look on us

Proxima Fisica Finis (1426) Nearest to natural end

Proxima Soli (1393) Nearest the sun

— R —

Raynaldus I Mut. Reg. E(c or r) D. XI MI. I. (1391) Rinaldo I eleventh duke of Modena and Reggio, and first of Mirandola

Rector Reip. Rhacusin (1637,9) Rector of the Republic of Ragusa

Reg. Cap. Bo. et de Liechtenstein Comes (1227,9,30) Count of the Royal Chapel of Bohemia and Liechtenstein

Reg. Cap. Bo. et de Schrattenbach Comes (1214) same but of Schrattenbach

Reg. Cap. Bohem. et de Troyer Comes (1231) same but of Troyer

Regi Svo Avgvstissimo iter in Hassiam Mense Ivn. A. MDCCXXXI Apparanti Felicem Favstamque et Profectionem et Reditionem A Deo Cvncta Svecia Svppliciter Precatvr (1726) For its most august king, preparing a journey to Hesse in the month of June in the year 1731, all Sweden as suppliant prays God for happy and fortunate going and returning

Regne de la Loi (1335-6) Rule of the law

Religione Defensa (1489) Religion being defended

Rep(ublica) Romana (1483-7) Roman Republic

Repubblice Ligure Anno I (1371) Ligurian Republic year I

Repubblica Napolitan(a) (1410) Neapolitan Republic

Republique Franco(a)ise (1336-7) Republic of France

Republique Genevoise (1768) Republic of Geneva

Respubl. Rhacus(i) (1640-1) Republic of Ragusa

Respublica Basiliensis (1758) Republic of Basel

Respublica Bernensis (1759-60) Republic of Bern

Respublica Genevensis (1767) Republic of Geneva

Respublica Lucernensi (1775) Republic of Luzern

Respublica Veneta (1552,6,62,3,8,75) Republic of Venice

Rex Sic(iliae) et Hie(r). (1411-2) King of Sicily and Jerusalem

— S —

S. Annae Fundgruben Ausb. Tha. In N. Oe. (1113) St. Anne mine, mining taler in Lower Austria

S. Ap. S. Leg. Nat(us) Germ. Primas (1249,55,7) Legate of the Holy Apostolic See, born Primate of Germany

S.C.M. Cons. Int. Cam. Supr. R. Boh. Praef. Burgg. Egr. (1191) Privy counselor of his sacred imperial majesty, high chamberlain of the kingdom of Bohemia, and burgrave of Eger

S.C.M. Cons. Status Int. & Haered. Per. Styr. Sup. Stab. Praefectus (1202) Privy and hereditary state counselor of his sacred, imperial majesty, high constable for Styria

S. Cyrill Prim. Apost. Morav. (1222) St. Cyril, first apostle of Moravia

S. Georgius Ferrariae Protec. (1439) St. George, protector of Ferrara

S.I. Aul. Reg. Her. & P. Ge. H. Post. Mag. (1193) Supreme of the Imperial court of the hereditary kingdom and provinces, general hereditary postmaster

S. Iochimbs. Thaler Ausbeuth (1137) St. Joachim's mining taler

S. Ioachimbsthalische Ausbeut Thaler 1074,7) St. Joachims Valley mining taler

S. Lambertus Patronus Leodiensis (1582-91) St. Lambert, patron of Liege

S.M.V(enetu) Aloy. Mocenico Dux (1525-8,36,7,58-61) St. Mark of Venice, Alvise Mocenigo, doge

S.M.V. Aloysius Pisani D. (1542-3) St. Mark of Venice, Alvise Pisani, doge

S.M.V. Carolus Ruzini D. (1539-40) St. Mark of Venice, Carlo Ruzzini, doge

S.M.V. Franc Lavredano Dux (1549-51) St. Mark of Venice, Francesco Loredan, doge

S.M.V(enet) Ioan Cornel(io) D(ux) (1531-4) St. Mark of Venice, Giovanni Corner, doge

S.M.V. Ludov(i) Manin Dux (1571-4) St. Mark of Venice, Lodovico Manin, doge

S.M.V. M(arc) Foscarenus D(ux) (1554-5) St. Mark of Venice, Marco Foscarini, doge

S.M.V. Paul Rainerius D(ux) (1565-7) St. Mark of Venice, Paolo Renier, doge

S.M.V. Petrus Grimani D. (1545-7) St. Mark of Venice, Pietro Grimani, doge

S. Maria Mater Dei Patrona Hung. (1125-33,68,9,72,4,7,9) Holy Mary, Mother of God, patron of Hungary

S. Petron(io) Prot(ector) Bon(on) (1464-6) St. Peter, protector of Bologna

S. Petronius Bon(on) Prot. (1467-70,5) same

S.R.I. Pr. Re. Cap. Boh. & A. Colloredo & Wald. Co. (1233) Prince of S.R.I., count of the royal chapel of Bohemia, and of Colloredo and Waldsee

S.R.I. Pr. Salisb. S.S. Ap. Leg. Nat. Germ. Primas (1247,56) Prince of S.R.I. of Salzburg, legate of the Holy Apostolic See, born primate of Germany

S.R.I. Princ. & Baro. Reteny Imp. (1482) Prince of S.R.I. and imperial baron of Retegno

S.R.I. Ps. R.C.B.C. Protect. Ger. S.C.R.M. Con. In. et Actval (1220-1,3-6) Prince of S.R.I., count of the royal chapel of Bohemia, protector of Germany, present privy counselor of his sacred, imperial, royal majesty

S. Rudbertus Eps. Salisburg (1234,6,8, 41) St. Rupert, bishop of Salzburg

S. Rupertus Episcop. Salisburgens (1243, 6,8,50-4) same

Sac. Rom. Imp. Archim. et Elect (1613,7) Grand Marshal and elector of S.R.I.

Salisburg S. Sed. Apos. Legat. Ger. Prim. (1240,2,4,5) Salzburg, legate of

the Holy Apostolic See, Primate of Germany

Salus Publica Salus Mea (1731-3) Public safety, my safety

Sanctus Leodegarius (1774) St. Leodegran

Sanctus Marcus Venet. (1524,9,30,5,8,41, 4,8,53,7,64,9,70) St. Mark of Venice

Sanctus Martinus (1373-6) St. Martin

Scudo Romano (1486) Roman scudo

Sede Vacante (1453,4,6,62,4,5) The See being vacant

Sigismundus D.G. Archiepiscop(us) (1247,51,6) Sigismund D.G. archbishop

Sigismundus D.G.A. (Episc.) & Pr. Salisburg (1249,55) as above and prince of Salzburg

Sigismund. D.G.A. & Pr. Sal. S.A.L. Nat. Germ. Primas (1248,50,2,4) as above and legate of the Apostolic See, born Primate of Germany

Sigismundus D.G.A. & P.S.A.S.L.N.G. P(rim). (1253,60) same

Sigm. D.G.A. & P.S.A.S.L.N.G. Prim. (1258,9,60) same

Sit Nomen Dom(ini) Benedict(um) (1316-34) Blessed be the name of the Lord

Soli Reduci (1408) To Him, the only one restored

Splendet in Orbe Decus (1725) Honor will shine in the world

Stanislaus Augustus D.G. Rex Pol(on) M.D. Lith(u) or Lit(uan) (1618-21,3) Stanislaus August, D.G. king of Poland, grandduke of Lithuania

Sub Tuum Praesidium Confug. (1234) We flee to Thy protection

Sup. Imp. Aul. Reg. Her. P.G. Her. Post. Mag. (1194) see S.I. Aul.

Supra Firmam Petram (1463) On a solid rock

Suum Cuique (1776) Let each have his own

— T —

Thomas Orciani F.T. S.R.I. Marchio Un. Cr. Bo. Com. & (1426-7) Thomas Orciano F.T. Marquis of S.R.I. and count of Hungary, Croatia, Bohemia ?

Tigurinae Moneta Reipublicae (1783,5, 6) Money of the Republic of Zürich

Traiectum ad Mosam (1854-5) The crossing of the Meuse

Troe love mod og hvad Dan. kongens gunst kand vinde mens Norge klippe har mand skal hos Nordmand finde (1301) Obedience to law, courage, and all that win the favor of the Danish king, you will find among the mountains of Norway and with the Norwegians

Tut. Mar. Gab. Pr. Vid. de Lobk. Nat. Pr. Sab.Car. et Aug. Pr. de Lobk. (1190) Regency of Maria Gabriele, widow of the prince of Lobkowitz, born princess of Savoy-Carignan, and August prince of Lobkowitz

— U —

Ubi Uvlt Spirat (1462) He breathes where he will

Union et Force (1337) Union and strength

Unum Omnium Votum Salus Principis S.P.Q.B. (1460) The safety of the prince is the prayer of all, the senate and the people of Bologna

Urbe Obsessa (1855) The city is besieged

Urokkelig som Dovres hoye fielde staaer Norges sonners troskab mod og vaelde (1312) Unmovable as the Dovres high mountains stand the loyalty, courage, and power of the sons of Norway

U.S.C. & R.A.M. Cons. Int. Gen. C. Mar. & Nob. Praet. H. Turmae Capit. (1187) Privy counselor of both their holy imperial and royal apostolic majesties, general field marshal and captain of the noble praetorian Hungarian squadrons

Utr. Sic. Hierus. (1396) The Two Sicilies, Jerusalem

— V —

Vdal. S.R.I. Pr. Ep. Cur. D. in Firstb. et Funaw. (1761) Ulrich, prince of S.R.I., bishop of Chur, lord in Firstenberg and Fürstenau

Veteris Monumentum Decoris (1392) A memorial of ancient honor

Vic. Am. D.G. Rex Sar. Cyp. et Ier. (1496-7) Victor Amadeus D.G. king of Sardinia, Cyprus, and Jerusalem

Victor Am. II D.G. Dux Sab. (1492) Victor Amadeus II D.G. Duke of Savoy

Viderunt Oculi mei Salutare Tuum (1432) Mine eyes have seen thy salvation

Vlrika Eleonora D.G. Regina Svec. (1718) Ulrica Eleonora D.G. queen of Sweden

Vox de Throno (1433-5) A voice from the throne

— W —

Wenceslaus S. Rom. Imp. Princeps a Paar (1194) Wenceslaus, prince of S.R.I. of Paar

Wolf(fg). D.G. S.R.E. Presb. Card. d(e) Schrattem(n)bach E(p). O(lom). Dux (1216-26) Wolffgang D.G. presbyter of the Holy Roman Church, Cardinal of Schrattenbach, bishop of Olmütz

Wolffgang D.G. S.R.E. Card. de Schrattembach Ep. Olom. (1215) Wolffgang D.G. of the Holy Roman Church, Cardinal of Schrattenbach, bishop of Olmütz

Wolffgangus D.G. Epus. Olomucensis Dux S.R.I.Prceps. (1214) Wolffgang D.G. bishop of Olmütz, duke, prince of S.R.I.

1 Rigsdaler Cour. (1312) 1 current rigsdaler

1 Rigsdaler Species (1313-5) 1 rigsdaler species

IIII Mark Danske (1291,4,6) 4 Danish marks

X Ex Marca Pura Colonien (1618-20) 10 to the fine Cologne mark

10-7/16 Ex Marca Pura Coloniens(i). (1621-2) 10-7/16 to the fine Cologne mark

XI Auf I. Feine Mark (1798) 11 to 1 fine mark

XII Florins IX Sols (1769-70) 12 florins, 11 sols

14-1/12 Ex Marca Pur. Coloniens. (1623) 14-1/12 to the fine Cologne mark

60 Schilling Schlesw. Holst. Courant (1311) 60 current Schleswig-Holstein schillings

APPENDIX B

Initials of Mintmasters, Etc.

mm.—mintmaster   med.—medalist   eng.—engraver
d.c.—die cutter   dir.—director   war.—warden
sup.—superintendent   ass.—assayer

The mm. in Venice were mint inspectors.

A.B.—Antonio Maria Beneventi eng. at Modena and Bologna 1720-24;
    Alvise Barbaro mm. Venice 1751-52;
    Andrea Bon mm. Venice 1785-86
A.C.—Alvise Corner mm. Venice 1786-87; Antonio Cicogna mm. Venice 1793-94
A.C.F.—
A.D.—Antonio Diedo mm. Venice
A.F.—Avise Foscarini mm. Venice 1779-81
A.H.-G.S.—A. Jos. Hammerschmidt mm. Karlsburg 1765-80, G. Schickmayer war. Karls-
    burg 1777-80
A.K.—Andrei Kozberg mm. St. Petersburg 1793-95
A.L.—Albrekt Lindberg mm. Stockholm 1762-73
A.M.—Alvise Minotto mm. Venice 1714-15;
    Angelo Malipiero mm. Venice 1719-21
A.M.P.—Anzolo Maria Priuli mm. Venice 1775-77
A.O.—Angelo Orio mm. Venice 1785-86
A.P.—see P.A.; Anton Partenstein mm. Warsaw 1772-74;
    Joseph Anton Pichler eng. Naples 1779
A.P./M—
A-S—L. Aschpacher mm. Hall 1765-74 and John J. Stockmer war. Hall 1765-80
A.S.—
A.W.—Anton Widmann or Wideman d.c. and eng. Vienna 1762-79
A. Wideman—see above.
B.—Philipp Christoph von Becker d.c. Vienna 1725-32;
    Johann Ephraim Bauert d.c. Oldenburg, Altona, Copenhagen 1761-99
B.C.—Benetto Capello mm. Venice 1769-71
B. Cotel—Bartolomeo Cotel eng. Ferrara 1706-18
B. Duviv. F.—Benjamin Duvivier (fecit) d.c. Paris 1764-95
B.H.—Bastion Hille mm. Rendsburg 1716-26
B-I—
B.K.—Vasili Klimentov d.c. St. Petersburg 1775
Borner F.—Peter Paul Borner (fecit) eng. Rome c. 1691-c. 1725
B.P.—see Perger
B.V.—Benetto Valier mm. Venice 1731-33
B.W.—Bernhard Wonsiedler mm. Kuttenberg 1702-16
B.Z.—Bortolomio Zeno mm. Venice 1733-34
C.—see C.F.
C.A.—Stepan Afonasiev mm. St. Petersburg 1764-70
C-A—Karlsburg mint, Zaragosa mm.
C.B.—Christoph Brettschneider mm. Brieg 1669-1713
C.C.—Conte Cappola dir. Naples 1760-94
C.F.—Cotel fecit see B. Cotel;
    Carlo Falconi eng. Bologna 1712-13
C-F—Carlos Tiburcio de Roxas and Francisco Lopez Amesa ass. Seville c. 1770-90
C-H—Pressburg mint
C.H.L.—Caspar Henrik Lyng mm. Copenhagen 1783-97
C-N—Carlos Tiburcio de Roxas and Nicolas Lamas ass. Seville 1792-1803
C.P.—
C.S.H.—Christ. Sigmund Hunger mm. Pressburg 1685-1709
C W—Copenhagen mint
D.—Georg Raphael Donner d.c. Vienna 1726, see J.D.
D.D.—Domenico Diedo mm. Venice 1715-17
DEG—de Gianelli d.c. Naples 1731-68

D.F.—Daniel Fehrman d.c. Stockholm 1739-1754
D.G.—see DEG; Domenico Gritti mm. Venice 1762-63
D.I.—David Ahron Jacobsen d.c. Altona 1787-88
D.I.A.—Daniel Jensen Adzer d.c. Copenhagen 1763
D.L.—
D.M.—
Dupré—Augustin Dupré eng. Paris 1791-1803
E.—see E.I.
E.B.—Ephraim Brenn mm. Warsaw 1774-92
E.D.C.—Ernest Dietrich Croll d.c. Leipzig 1753-56, Dresden 1763-78
E.H.—see Hameran
E.I.—Egor Ivanov mm. Moscow 1752-69
E.P.H.—Ernest Peter Hecht eng. Leipzig 1702-03
EvM-D—Edl. von Münzburg mm. Kremnitz 1765-74 and Paschal Jos. von Damiani war.
        Kremnitz 1765-80
EvS-A.S.—Erdmann von Schwingerschuh mm. Prague 1755-84 and Anton Stehr war.
        Prague 1765-73
EvS-I.K.—Schwingerschuh as above and Ign. Kandler war. Prague 1773-80
F.—see D.F.; Fernando Vazquez ass. Segovia 1727-29, Madrid 1730-
F.A.—
F.A.F.—Francesco Antonio Foscarini mm. Venice 1742-43
F.A.P.—Francesco Antonio Paruta mm. Venice 1709-10
F.B.—Filippo Balucani d.c. Bologna 1774-   , Francesco Barattani eng. Bologna
        c. 1775; Francesco Barbaro mm. Venice 1796-97
F.B./A.—
F.D.—Francesco Dandolo mm. Venice 1782-84, Fantino Dandolo mm. Venice 1784-85
F.M.—see below
(F.)M.K.—Franz Xaver Matzenkopf d.c. Salzburg 1738-44
F.M.S.—
F.N.—Franz Nowak war. Oppeln 1699-1704, mm. Breslau 1704-23;
        Francesco Notarbartolo mm. Palermo 1734-49
F.P.—Francesco Pasqualigo mm. Venice 1741-42
F.R.—Francesco Maria Rizzi mm. Venice 1786-87
F.S.—Ferdinand Scharf mm. Prague 1713-46;
        Friedrich Sylm mm. Warsaw 1765-67
F-S—Jos. Faby mm. Günzburg 1788-1805 and Fr. Stehr war. Günzburg   -1797
F. Seuo—Ferdinando Sevo eng. Rome 1706
F.S.L.—
F.W.—Franz Xaver Würth d.c. Vienna 1745-1790
G.—Maria Antonio Gennaro d.c. Vienna 1723-27; Gouin eng. Moscow 1707-10;
        Paul H. Gödicke med. Hamburg 1730-1764
G.A.—
G.A.C.—Giacomo Antonio Contarini mm. Venice 1751-53
G.A.F.—Giacomo Angelo Foscarini mm. Venice 1772-73
G.A.S.—Georg Anton Schröder mm. Rethwisch in Plön 1761
G-B—
G.E.—Gregor Egerer mm. Prague 1694-1710
G.F.—Gerolamo Foscarini mm. Venice 1786-88; Giacomo Foscarini mm. Venice 1788-89
G.F.N.—Georg Friedrich Nürnberger mm. Nuremberg 1682-1724
G.H.—
G. Hamerani—see Hameran
G.L.-C.—Gabr. Lancilotto Castello mm. Palermo 1775-1790
G.L.-C.I.—same as preceding, temporary, Palermo 1791
G.M.B.—Giustiniano Maria Badoer mm. Venice 1773-75
G.P.—Giacomo Pasqualigo mm. Venice 1773-74
G.T.K.—
G.T.S.—Gian Tomaso Soranzo mm. Venice 1701-02
G.Z.—Georg Zedritz mm. Stockholm 1722-38
H.—see I.H. and J.H.; Gert Hall d.c. Altona 1788; Haupt eng. Moscow 1707-09
H-A—Hall mint
Hameran(us)(i)—Ermenegildo Hameranus eng. Rome 1705-44
        Ottone Hameranus eng and mm. Rome 1734-68
        Giocchimo Hameranus eng. Rome 1798-99
H.C.M.—Henning Christopher Meyer mm. Kongsberg   -1717;
        Henrik Christopher Meyer mm. Kongsberg   -1727

Herman(ig)—see Hameranus, E.
H.I.A.B.—Hans Jacob Arnold Branth mm, Kongsberg 1776-97, Copenhagen 1797
H.I.G.—Hans Jacob Gessner (father) mm. Zurich 1706-36; (son) same 1745-70
H.K.—Nazar Kutuzov mm. St. Petersburg 1758-63
HL—Johann Karl Hedlinger d.c. Luzern 1713-15
H.L.C.—
H.M.—Hans Malmberg mm. Stockholm 1738-62; see also I.H.
H.S.K.—Hans Schierven Knoph mm. Copenhagen 1761-83
H. Vassallo—eng. Genoa 1797-1808
H.Z.—Heinrich Zedritz mm. Stockholm 1700-06
I.A.K.—Johann Ant. König eng. Hall 1684-1746
I.A.P.—J.A. Putz mm. Prague 1711-13; J.A. Pöhl d.c. Prague 1717
I.B.M.—
I.C.—Ivan Sabelnikov mm. St. Petersburg 1796
I.C.-F.A.—Johan August von Cronberg mm. Vienna 1766-80 and Franz Aicherau war.
     Vienna 1774-80
I.C.-S.K.—as above and Sig. Klemmer war. Vienna 1765-76
I.C. Roettiers—Joseph Charles Roettiers eng. Paris 1727-53
I.D.B.—Justinus or Johann de Beyer eng. Bern c. 1698-1738
I.G.R.—Johann Georg Ritter war. Prague 1713-14
I.G.S.—Johan Georg Seidlitz d.c. Vienna c. 1700-1730
I.H.—Johann Handmann d.c. Basel 1740-69
I.H.W.—Johann Henrik Wolf d.c. Copenhagen 1764-65
I.K.-S.C.—probably an error for I.C.-S.K.
I.L.—Jean Leefken eng. Moscow 1705-09; Jean Lang eng. Moscow 1718-19
I.L.L.—see I.L. (1)
I.M.—Ivan Markov mm. St. Petersburg 1751-58
I.M.H.—Johann Mich. Hofmann d.c. Vienna 1680-1736
I.N. Wirt F.—Johann Nep. Wirt (fecit) d.c. Vienna 1788-94
I.P.—Jean Patry eng. Geneva c. 1712-29
I.S.—Justus Carl Schröder mm. Warsaw 1768-72
I. Toda—Josef Toda d.c. Vienna 1764-70
I.V.—see I.Z.V.
I. Veber—see I.Z.V.
I.W.—see I.N. Wirt
I.Z.V.—Johann Zanobia Weber eng. Vienna 1761, d.c. Florence 1770-86
J.D.—J. Dobeck med. Olmütz c. 1740
J-F—José Garcia Cabellero, Fernando Vazquez ass. Madrid c. 1730
J.H.—see I.M.H.
J.J.—Juan José Cabellero ass. Madrid c. 1706-29
J.M.—
J-P—Juan Rodriguez Gutierrez and Pedra Cano ass. Madrid c. 1762-74
J-V—José de Villaviciosa and Vicente Diaz de la Fuente ass. Seville 1762
J.V.I.—Giuseppe Ugo, temporary, mm. Palermo 1798-1807
K.—see O.K.
K-B—Kremnitz mint
K.O.—see O.K.
L.—see I.L.; C. F. Lüders med. Berlin c. 1702-1742
L.A.F.—Lunardo Alvise Foscarini mm. Venice 1777-79
L.B.—Lorenzo Bonlini mm. Venice 1774-75
L.C.—Lorens Carulberg mm. Stockholm 1706-22
L.S.—Luigi (Lodovico) Siries (Series) (fecit) d.c. Tuscany 1747-79
L.S.F.—see above
M.—see F.M.K.; Maxen or Marenz d.c. Altona 1788-99; Madrid mintmark
M.A.T.—Marco Antonio Trevisan mm. Venice 1771-73
M.B.—Marin Bembo mm. Venice 1717-18
M.F.—Michael Flor mm. Altona 1786-1818;
     Manuel de Lames and Francisco Herrera ass. Madrid c. 1788-1802
M.F./A.—
M.H.—see I.M.H.
M-J—Madrid mint and José Cabellero ass. Madrid c. 1706-29
M.K.—see F.M.K.
M.K.-F.M.—see F.M.K.
M.M.—Marchese Mazzaro sup. Naples 1747; Michail Michailov mm. St. Petersburg
     1783-84

M.S.—Michele Soranzo mm. Venice 1735-37
M-S—M. Cassayer ass. Seville and Seville mint
M.V.—
N-B—Nagybanya mint
N.d'.-O.V.—Nicola d'Orgemont Vigevi mon. Palermo 1793-98
O. Hamerani—see Hameran
O.K.—Otfrid Koenig eng. Moscow 1718-25
O.L.—Olof Lidiin mm. Stockholm 1773-1819
O.M.—Osip Medsher mm. St. Petersburg 1798-1801
P.—see Perger; see S-P
P-A—Pedro Remigio Gordillo and Antonio Montero ass. Seville c. 1731-35
P.C.W.—Peter Christian Winslow d.c. Copenhagen 1749
P.D.—Piero Donà mm. Venice 1776-77
P.G.—Peter Leonhard Gianelli d.c. Copenhagen 1798-1807
Perg(er)—Bernardo Perger d.c. Naples 1769-1798
P.J.—see J.P.
P.M.—Vacant in Prague 1710-11; Piero Magno mm. Venice 1701-02;
     Piero Manolesso mm. Venice 1702-03; Piero Mososini mm. Venice 1707-09
P.P.B.—see Borner
P-R—Prague mint
P.S.-I.F.—error for T.S.?, see T.S.-I.F.
P.S.-I.K.—Paul Erdmann von Schwingerschuh mm. Prague 1755-84 and Ign. Kindler
     war. Prague 1773-80
P.T.—Petronio Tadolini eng. Bologna 1775-1800; Pietro Termanini Modena
P.W.—Paul Wödröde war. Pressburg 1709-21
R.—Ruffo war. Naples 1747
R.B.—Raimondo Bembo mm. Venice 1779-80; Rizzardo Balbi mm. Venice 1780-81
R.B.P.—Rizzardo Balbi Primo mm. Venice 1768-69
R. Dag.—
S.—See Silipra; Seville mintmark; Anton Schäfer (Schaffer) mm. and d.c. Mannheim
     1744-99
S.B.—Stefano Barbaro mm. Venice 1753-54
S-B—San Biagio
S-C—Tobias Schöbl mm. Günzburg 1762-88 and Hubert Cotz war. Günzburg 1765-74
S.F.—see L.S.F.
S-F—Tobias Schöbl mm. Günzburg 1762-88 and Jos. Faby war. Günzburg 1774-88
Silipra—Giuseppe Siliprandi d.c. Parma 1784-87
S.I.—Salomon Ahron Jacobsen d.c. Kongsberg 1792
S.K.-P.D.—Sigmund A. Klemmer mm. Kremnitz 1774-80, and Pascal Damiani war.
     Kremnitz 1765-80
S-M—Seville mint and M. Cassayer ass. Seville; silver money (Swedish)
S.M.—Simone Maurigi mm. Palermo c. 1725-34
S-P—Seville mint and Pedro Remigio Gordillo ass. Seville
S—Prins
ST.—
S.V.R.—Ferdinando di St. Urbain eng. Rome 1683-1702
T.B.—Thomas Bernard d.c. Paris 1678-1716;
     Théodore Bonneton med. Geneva c. 1788-1805
T.F.—G. Toda (fecit) d.c. Prague 1759
T.L.—Truela Andersen Lyng mm. Kongsberg 1746-66
T.M.—Tommaso Mercandetti eng. Rome 1796-1821
T.S.-I.F.—Tobias Schöbl mm. Günzburg 1762-88 and Jos. Faby war. Günzburg 1774-88
V.C.-S.—J.H. von Clotz war. Hall 1775-80 and J. J. Stockner war. Hall 1765-80
V.I.—Josef Vinoges Vinazer eng. Kremnitz 1796-1814
V.M./A.—Virgillo Martenise mm. Naples c. 1730 and Ariani war. Naples
V.Q.—Vincenzo Querini mm. Venice 1722-23
V.S.—Valerio Soranza mm. Venice 1777-78
V.V.—Valerio Valier mm. Venice 1775-76
W.—see A. Widman or P.C.W.
W-I—Vienna mintmark
Z.D.—Zuanne Dolfin mm. Venice 1761-62
Z.F.—Zorzi Foscolo mm. Venice 1734-35
Z.V.—see I.Z.V.; Venice mint

APPENDIX C

PSEUDO CROWNS

AUSTRIAN NETHERLANDS

1861   DUCATON 1751

M.T.D.G.R. IMP. G.H. - B. REG. A.A.D. BURG., bust of Maria Theresia R with hand (Antwerp mm.) and 1751 below.
FRANC. D.G.R.I.S. - A.G.E. IER. R. LO. B.M.H.D., bust of Francis I R.
Supposedly for a visit to the mint. Also in gold.

1862   DUCATON 1751

FRANC. D.G.R.I.S. - A. GE. IER. LO. B.M.H.D., bust R.
JN. TE DOMINE. - SPERAVI. 1751. hand, crowned double eagle with arms on breast in chain of the Golden Fleece.

DENMARK

There are 1 krone pieces of 1701, 1702, 1747, 1748, and 1771 all less than 20 grams in weight.

HOLSTEIN

1863   1½, 1 TALER 1702

FRID. D.G. HAER. NOR. DVX. - SL. HOL. ST. E. DIT. COM. I. OLD. E. DEL., bust of Frederik IV R.
LABORE. ET. CONSTANTIA *, in center NATVS / A.C. MDCLXXI. D. 18. OCT. / OCCVB. IN. PRAELIO. CONT. / REGEM. POL. AD. CLISSOV. / D.9/19.IVL. A. MDCCII. A. REG. / VIII. AET. XXXI. M.8.D. XXI / HEU. PRAEPOSTERA / FATA !
Medallic talers on the death of the Duke.

ITALY

GENOA

1864   4 LIRE 1709, 1710, 1712, 1716

.DUXET. GVBER. REIPV. GENVEN., crowned and supported arms.
NON SVRREXIT MAIOR * date, initials, St. John the Baptist preaching.
Weigh 20 gr.

MANTUA

1865   TALER 1765

There is apparently a siege piece struck in 1796 of the Maria Theresia taler 1765 just like the regular issue.

MODENA

1866   SCUDO 1717-1719

RAYNALDVS. I. MUT.R.M. EC. DVX., bust of Rinaldo R with .date. below.
NOBILITAS - ESTENSIS., crowned eagle with arms on breast and 103 below.
Weigh 16 gr.

PAPACY

The scudos of 1742 and 1775 (Testa 163 and 172) are omitted, the first as a medal, the second as non-existent.

SAVOY-SARDINIA

1867   3 LIRE 1717-1718

VIC. AM. D.G. SIC. IER. ET. CYP. REX., bust of Victor Amadeus R.
DVX. SAB. ET. MON - TISF. PRIN. PED. &. date *, crowned arms with S. 60 below.
Weigh 18.25 gr.

VENICE

1868   LEONE FOR THE MARITIME PROVINCES 1736

ALOY* PISANI* D* - S * M * VENETVS, standing and kneeling figures with * 1736 * in exergue
PROVINCIJS MARITIMIS DATVM., harbor scene with XII below.
Weigh 19 gr. There are two types.

POLAND

1869 TALER 1705
D.G. FRIDERICVS AVGVSTVS REX POLON. ET ELECT. SAXON., bust R.
RESTAVRATOR ORDINIS AQVILAE POLONICAE. star in ribbon with another star suspended.
A medal for the restoration of the Polish Order of the White Eagle. (HC 2710)

RAGUSA

1870 SCUDO 1708-1709
* PROTECTOR. REIPVBLICAE. RHAGVSINAE, St. Biagio standing facing, separating S - B
and date at sides.
* TVTA. SALVS. SPES. ET. PRAESIDIVM., The Savior standing facing in circle of stars.
Weigh 17 gr.

1871 DUCATO (OLD) 1722-1723
DVCAT. REIP. - .RHACVSINAE, .crowned arms.
TVIS. A. DEO. - .AVSPICIIS., St. Biagio standing facing separating .S. - .B. and date at sides.
Weigh 19 gr.

SWEDEN

1872 REICHSTALER 1709
CAROL: XII D.G. SVEC. GOTH. VAND. REX PROPUGNATOR FIDEI. 1 Reichsthlr. nach
alten schr: u. korn., bust R.
COLLAPSAM FORTITER RESTITUIT. lion supporting burning candle. In xergue IN MEMOR.
TRACTAT. ALTRANSTAD / 22 AUGUST MDCCVII CONCLUSI. / ET BRESLAU D.8.
FEBR. / MDCCIX COM / PLETI
A medal struck in the city of Stettin in Pomerania to commemorate the signing of the religious
pact of Altranstadt in Breslau.
There are 4 marks coins of Charles XII 1701-1705, 1708-1716 in two types; Ulrika Eleonora
1720; Frederik I 1720, 1732, 1737-1738 in three types; Adolphus Frederik 1752-1755. These
weigh about 21 gr.

SWITZERLAND

BERN

1873 SECHZEHNERPFENNIG 1700-1776
SENATUS. ET. SEDECIM. VIRI. REIPUB. BERNENSIS., bear to L.
LIBERTAS - LIBE - RIS - CURAE, two arms clasping with swords under wreath and radiant
triangle.
There are three general types of these medals.

GRAUBUNDEN

1874 TALER 1706
Three oval shields in a cartouche, all inside a wreath.
Lion of Venice with sword to L within wreath. 1706 below.
A medal to commemorate the alliance with the Republic of Venice..

UNTERWALDEN

1875 TALER 1729
MONETA REIP. SUBSYLVANIA SUPERIORIS ! 1729 *, arms in cartouche.
B. NICOLAUS . von. FLUE. NAT. OB. 1488, bust R.

1876 TALER 1732
IBI UNABAM ET. / ORABAM ANTE / FACIEM DEI. — 2. ESDR. 2 / IN EXPOSITIONE *.
/ MDCCXXXII. in sprays under crowned head in circles.
Similar to #1780.

BIBLIOGRAPHY

The general sources for historical, genealogical, biographical, geographical, and legend material are those listed in the earlier volume of this series. All the comprehensive numismatic works have likewise been previously cited. The specific sources of information for the various countries included in this volume are described below.

AUSTRIA (HABSBURGS, PRINCES, CHURCH RULERS)
Bernhart, Max and Roll, Karl, *Die Münzen und Medaillen des Erzstiftes Salzburg*, 2 vols., Munich, 1930.
Cejnek, R. Josef, *Österreichische Münzprägungen von 1519-1935*, 2 vols. and supplement, Vienna 1935, 1954
Holzmair, Eduard, "Münzgeschichte der österreichischen Neufürsten," *Numismatische Zeitschrift*, LXXI (1946), 6-73.
Jaeckel, Peter, *Die Münzprägungen des Hauses Habsburg 1780-1918*, Basel, 1956.
Mayer, Eduard E. von, *Des Fürstlichen Hochstiftes Olmütz Münzen und Medaillen*, Vienna 1873.
Miller zu Aichholz, V. von, Loehr, A., and Holzmair, E., *Österreichische Münzprägungen 1519-1938*, 2 vols., Vienna 1948.
Probszt, Günther, *Die Münzen Salzburgs*, Graz 1959.

DENMARK
Schou, H. H. *Beskrivelse af Danske og Norske Monter 1448-1814 og Danske Monter 1815-1923*, 2 vols., Copenhagen 1926.
Wilcke, J., *Kurantmonten 1726-1788*, Copenhagen, 1927.
Wilcke, J., *Specie-Kurant og Rigsbankdaler 1788-1845*, Copenhagen, 1929.

FRANCE
Ciani, Louis, *Les Monnaies Royales Francaises de Hugues Capet a Louis XVI*, Paris, 1926.
Guilloteau, V., *Monnaies Francaises*, Paris, 1943.
Raymond, Wayte, *The Silver Ecus of France*, New York, 1940.

GREAT BRITAIN
Raymond, Wayte, *The Silver Crowns of Great Britain and Ireland*, New York, 1941.
Seaby, H. A., *The English Silver Coinage from 1649*, London, 1957.
Spink & Son, *The Milled Coinage of England, 1662-1946*, London, 1950.

HOLSTEIN
Lange, Christian, *Sammlung Schleswig-holsteinischer Münzen und Medaillen*, 2 vols., Berlin, 1908, 1912.

ITALIAN STATES
Cagiati, Memmo, *Le Monete del Reame delle Due Sicilie*, 10 fasc., Naples, 1911-1937.
Corpus Nummorum Italicorum, 20 vols., Rome, 1910-1947.
Galeotti, Arrigo, *Le Monete del Granducato di Toscana*, Leghorn, 1930.
Gnecchi, Francesco and Ercole, *Le Monete di Milano*, and supplement, Milan, 1884, 1894.

Rinaldi, Oscar, *Le Monete coniate in Italia dalla Rivoluzione Francese ai nostri Giorni*, Mantua, 1954.
Spahr, Rodolfo, *Le Monete Siciliane dagli Aragonesi ai Borboni 1282-1836*, Palermo, 1959.
Testa, Girolamo Spaziani, *Ducatoni, Piastre, Scudi, Talleri e loro multipli battuti in zecche italiane e da italiani all' estero*, 2 vols., I. Casa Savoia, Rome, 1951, II. Romani Pontefici, Rome, 1952.

LIECHTENSTEIN
Holzmair, see Austria.
Missong, Alex., "Die Münzen des Fürstenhauses Liechtenstein," *Numismatische Zeitschrift*, XIV (1882), pp. 109-190.

LIEGE
Chestret de Haneffe, J. de, *Numismatique de la Principaute de Liege*, and supplement, Brussels, 1890, 1900.
Renesse-Breidbach, Comte de, *Histoire Numismatique de l'Eveche et Principaute de Liege*, Brussels, 1831.

LUXEMBURG
Bernays, E. and Vannerus, J., *Histoire numismatique du Comte puis Duche de Luxembourg et de ses Fiefs*, and supplement, Brussels, 1910, 1934.

MALTA
Schembri, H. C., *Coins and Medals of the Knights of Malta*, London, 1908.

POLAND
Gumowski, Marian, *Handbuch der polnischen Numismatik*, Cracow, 1914
Hutten-Czapski, Emeric, *Catalogue de la Collection des Medailles et Monnaies Polonaises*, 5 vols., St. Petersburg and Cracow, 1871-1916.

PORTUGAL
Batalha Reis, P., *Precario das Moedas Portuguesas de 1140-1940*, Lisbon, 1956.
Ferraro Vaz, J. *Catalogo das Moedas Portuguesas 1640-1948*, Lisbon, 1948.

RAGUSA
Resetar, Milan, "Le Monete della repubblica di Ragusa," *Rivista Italiana di Numismatica*, XVIII (1905), 215-30.

RUSSIA
Kelpsh, Andrew E., "Rubles of Peter the Great," *Numismatist*, LXII (1949), 161-174.
Kelpsh, Andrew E., "Rubles of the Successors of Peter the Great," *Numismatist*, LXIII (1950), 495-512.

SPAIN
Dasi, Tomas, *Estudio de los Reales de a Ocho*, 5 vols., Valencia, 1950-51.
Enno Van Gelder, H. and Hoc, Marcel, *Les Monnaies des Pays-Bas Bourguignons et Espagnols 1434-1713*, Amsterdam, 1960.
Herrara, Adolfo, *El Duro*, 2 vols., Madrid, 1914.
Vidal Quadras y Ramon, Manuel, *Catalogo de la Coleccion de Monedas y Medallas*, 4 vols., Barcelona, 1892.
Yriarte, Jose de, *Catalogo de los Reales de a Ocho Espanoles*, Madrid, 1955.

SWEDEN

L. E. Brunn Sammlung Schwedische Münzen, Frankfurt (A. Hess), 1914.
Glück, Harry and Hesselblad, C. G., *Artalsförteckning över Svenska Mynt*, Stockholm, 1959.
Lindgren, Torgny, *Sveriges Mynt 1719-1776*, Stockholm, 1953.
J. F. H. Oldenburgs Samling, Stockholm, 1883.

SWITZERLAND

Coraggioni, Leodegar, *Münzgeschichte der Schweiz*, Geneva, 1896.
Demole, Eugene, *Histoire Monetaire de Geneve 1535-1848*, 2 vols., Geneva, 1887, 1892.
Demole, Eugene and Wavre, William, *Histoire monetaire de Neuchatel*, Neuchatel, 1939.
Geigy, Alfred, *Katalog der Basler Münzen und Medaillen*, (Ewig collection), Basel, 1899.
Haller, G. E. von, *Schweizerisches Münz-und Medaillenkabinet*, 2 vols., Bern, 1780-1781.
Hofer, Paul, *Die Münzprägungen der Helvetischen Republik*, Bern, 1936.
Jenner, E., *Die Münzen der Schweiz*, Bern, 1901.
Lohner, Carl, *Die Münzen der Republik Bern*, Zürich, 1846.
Trachsel, C. F., *Die Münzen und Medaillen Graubündens*, Berlin, 1866.
Wunderly von Muralt, Hans, *Die Münz-und Medaillen Sammlung des*, 5 vols., Zürich, 1896-1898.

TURKEY

Lane-Poole, Stanley, ed., *The Coins of the Turks in the British Museum*, Vol. VIII of the *Catalogue of Oriental Coins*, London, 1883.

UNITED NETHERLANDS

Schulman, Jacques, *Handboek van de Nederlandsche Munten van 1795-1945*, Amsterdam, 1946.
Van der Wiel, A., "De Nederlandse Munten 1576-1808," *Jaarboek van het Kon. Ned. Genootschap voor Munt- en Penningkunde*, XL (1953), 71-110.
Verkade, P., *Muntboek* etc., Schiedam, 1848.